DOG LEAD

3 LETTERS
CUR
RUN
VET

4 LETTERS
CHOW
COAT
NOSE
PEKE
PLAY
TROT

5 LETTERS
CAIRN
CORGI
DINGO
GROWL
HOUND
LEASH
POOCH
PUPPY
SPITZ

6 LETTERS
CANINE
COLLIE
KENNEL
POODLE
SETTER
SHOUGH

7 LETTERS
BARKING
POINTER
SPANIEL
TERRIER

8 LETTERS
AIREDALE
ALSATIAN
LABRADOR
SPRINGER
WATCHDOG

9 LETTERS
GREYHOUND

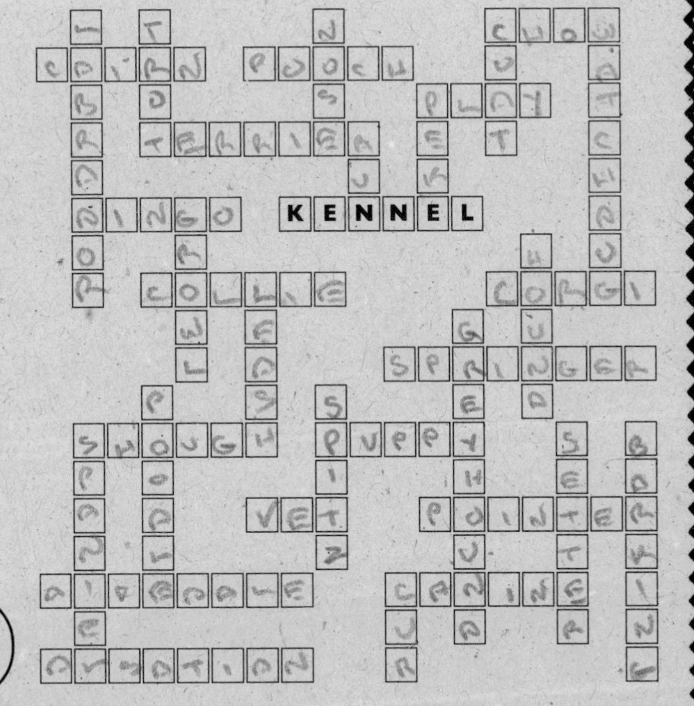

DESSERTED

3 LETTERS
RUM

4 LETTERS
CAKE
FLAN
LIME
PEAR
RICE
SAGO
SOUR
TART

5 LETTERS
CREAM
FRUIT
FUDGE
ICING
JELLY
LEMON
MELON
SCONE
SWEET

6 LETTERS
ALMOND
CLARET
CRISPS
ECLAIR
GATEAU
ORANGE
SPONGE
TOFFEE

7 LETTERS
COCONUT
DESSERT
PUDDING
TREACLE

8 LETTERS
APPLE PIE
DOUGHNUT
MERINGUE

12 LETTERS
VANILLA SLICE

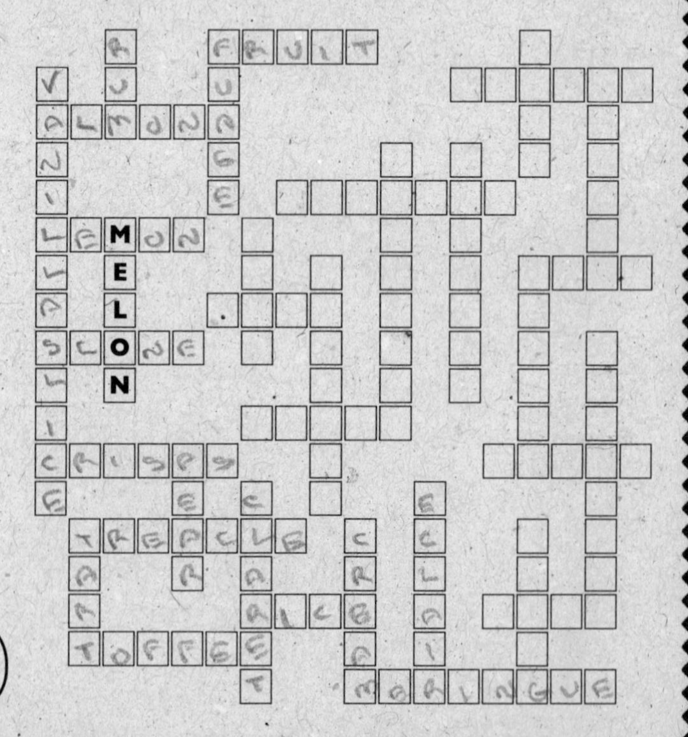

Y ENDING

3 LETTERS
ANY
BAY
CRY
DAY
IVY
KEY

4 LETTERS
GREY
MANY
PLAY

5 LETTERS
DALLY
EBONY
FUSSY
MALAY
MOGGY
SHINY
SNOWY
STONY

6 LETTERS
BOUNTY
ENTITY
HOCKEY
INJURY
JERSEY
REALLY

7 LETTERS
COOKERY
GRANDLY
NAUGHTY
ORDERLY
OVERTLY
SEVENTY
SURGERY
TENANCY
TYRANNY
UTILITY
VICEROY

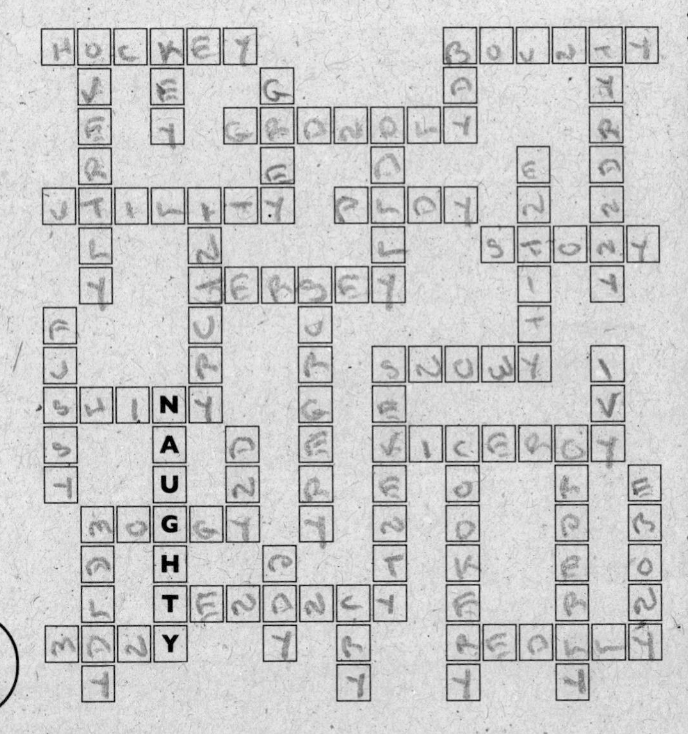

CLUELESS

Fit the words in the grid, then make an answer to the clue in the shaded squares.
Shaded clue: Planet.

4 LETTERS
ACHE
EPIC
PLUS
SEAM
TENT
YOKE

5 LETTERS
COMBS
ESSAY
EVADE
PLANT
RACED
SPEAK

6 LETTERS
CATNAP
ENDURE
MOMENT
RELICS
STATIC
TACKLE

7 LETTERS
INERTIA
PACKAGE
PLAYING
STEEPLE

8 LETTERS
BEETROOT
CARNIVAL

9 LETTERS
GOSSIPERS
PLUMPNESS

10 LETTERS
FRIENDLESS
ATTEMPTING

11 LETTERS
MICROFILMED

ROAM & RAMBLE

3 LETTERS
FLY
LIE
RUN

4 LETTERS
EDGE
HOLD
LOLL
PARK
PASS
RAID
REST
ROAM
ROLL
SCUD

5 LETTERS
COAST
DODGE
DRIFT
DWELL
FLITS
GLIDE
KNEEL
MARCH
MOORS
PAUSE
PROWL
SKATE
SLIDE
SPEED
STALL
TARRY
TOURS
TRIPS

6 LETTERS
ANCHOR
ARRIVE
BROODS
CAREER
DEPART
LIGHTS
LINGER
PULL UP
RAMBLE
REPOSE
STREAM
TODDLE
WANDER

7 LETTERS
CRUISES
LOITERS
MEANDER
PATROLS
RESIDES
TRAVELS

11 LETTERS
PERAMBULATE

SIZE WISE

3 LETTERS
BIG
WEE

4 LETTERS
HUGE
MINI
PUNY
TINY
VAST

5 LETTERS
GIANT
GREAT
LARGE
SMALL
TEENY
TICHY
WEENY

6 LETTERS
LITTLE
MINUTE
PETITE
SLIGHT

7 LETTERS
MAMMOTH
TITANIC

8 LETTERS
COLOSSAL
ENORMOUS
GIGANTIC

9 LETTERS
ITSY-BITSY
MINIATURE
PINT-SIZED

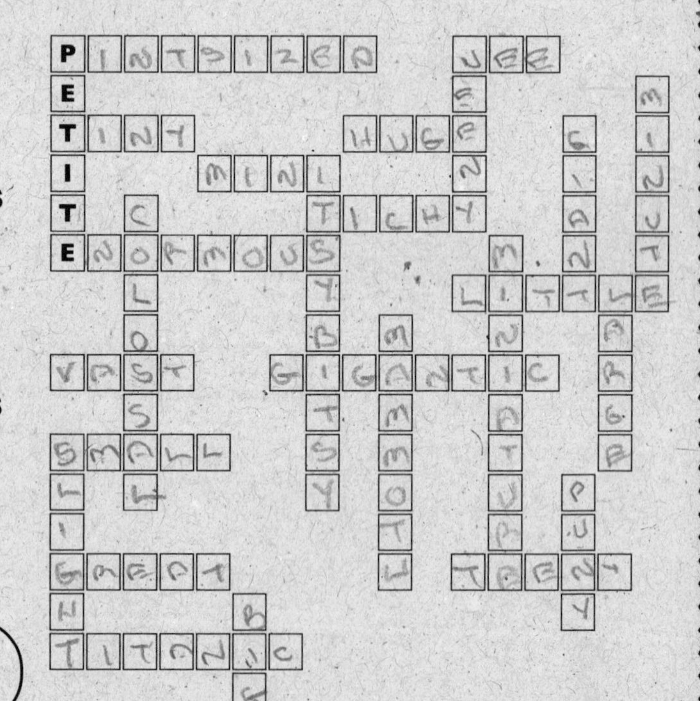

SOUPER DOOPER

3 LETTERS
CAN
CUP
HOT
PAN
PEA

4 LETTERS
BOWL
HEAT
HERB
LEEK
POUR
RICH
SOUP
STIR

5 LETTERS
AROMA
BROTH
CLEAR
ENJOY
SPICY
SPOON
TASTY
THICK

6 LETTERS
LENTIL
ONIONS
PACKET
POTATO
TOMATO

7 LETTERS
CARROTS
FILLING
FLAVOUR
INSTANT

8 LETTERS
BROCCOLI
CROUTONS
MUSHROOM

9 LETTERS
ASPARAGUS
CONDENSED

10 LETTERS
MINESTRONE

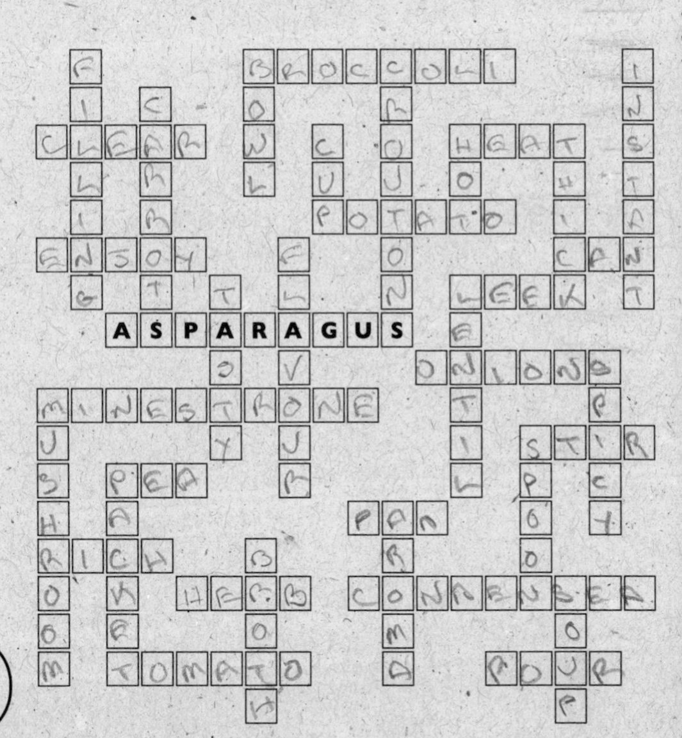

ON A MUSICAL NOTE

3 LETTERS
DUO
SAX

4 LETTERS
BASS
DRUM
DUET
FIFE
FORM
GONG
HORN
LUTE
NOTE
OBOE
SOLO
TIME
TUBA
VIOL

5 LETTERS
BANJO
BASSO
BELLS
BUGLE
ETUDE
FLUTE
ORGAN
PIANO
REEDS
THEME
VIOLA

6 LETTERS
CHIMES
OPERAS
TATTOO
VIOLIN

7 LETTERS
BASSOON
CYMBALS
HARMONY
MANDOLA
PICCOLO
SYMBOLS
TABORET

8 LETTERS
MANDOLIN
PLECTRUM
QUARTETS
TROMBONE

9 LETTERS
ORCHESTRA
XYLOPHONE

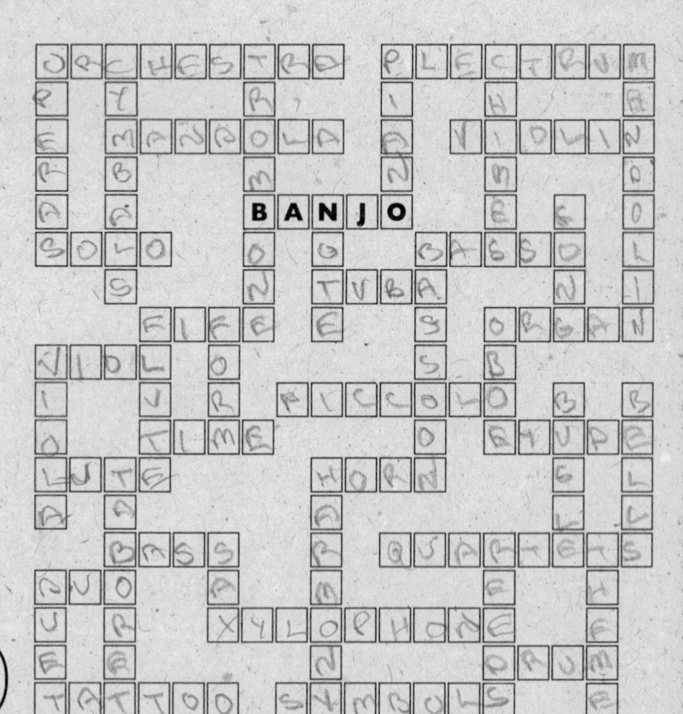

JEWELLERY BOX

3 LETTERS
JET
PIN

4 LETTERS
BEAD
GEMS
JADE
OPAL
RING
RUBY

5 LETTERS
CAMEO
CLASP
PASTE
STONE
TOPAZ

6 LETTERS
BANGLE
BROOCH
CHARMS
CHOKER
JEWELS
LOCKET

7 LETTERS
CRYSTAL
DIAMOND
EARRING
PENDANT

8 LETTERS
AMETHYST
BRACELET

9 LETTERS
SOLITAIRE

13 LETTERS
LAPIS NECKLACE
PEARL NECKLACE

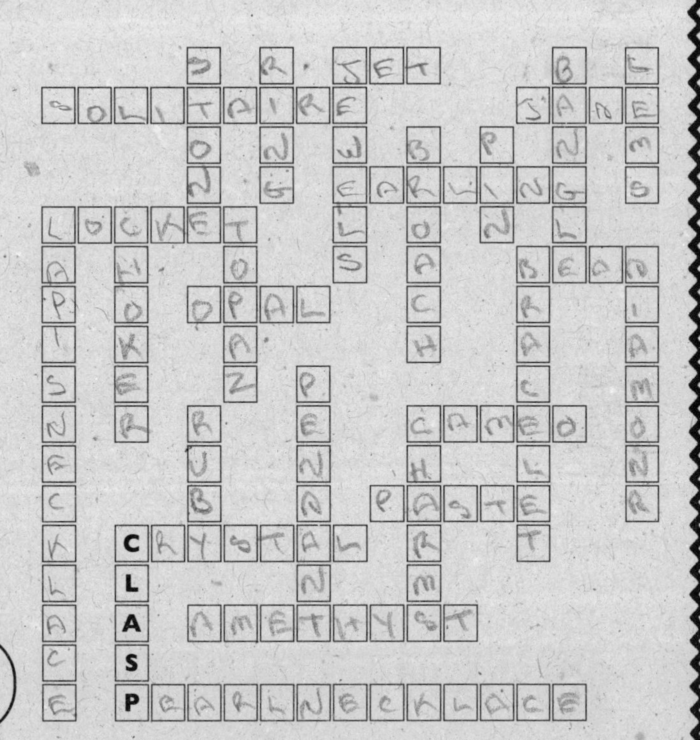

PARTY TIME

3 LETTERS
AGE
BOY
EAT
HAT
TEA

4 LETTERS
BLOW
CAKE
CHEW
FOOD
GIFT
GIRL
GIVE
ICES
KIDS
LOVE
TALK
TUNE
WRAP

5 LETTERS
CARDS
CREAM
DRINK
FRUIT
GAMES
HAPPY
ICING
JELLY
LIGHT
NOISE
PARTY

6 LETTERS
CHAIRS
CRISPS
SWEETS
TRICKS

7 LETTERS
DESSERT
PRESENT
WELCOME

8 LETTERS
BALLOONS
BIRTHDAY
ICE CREAM
LEMONADE

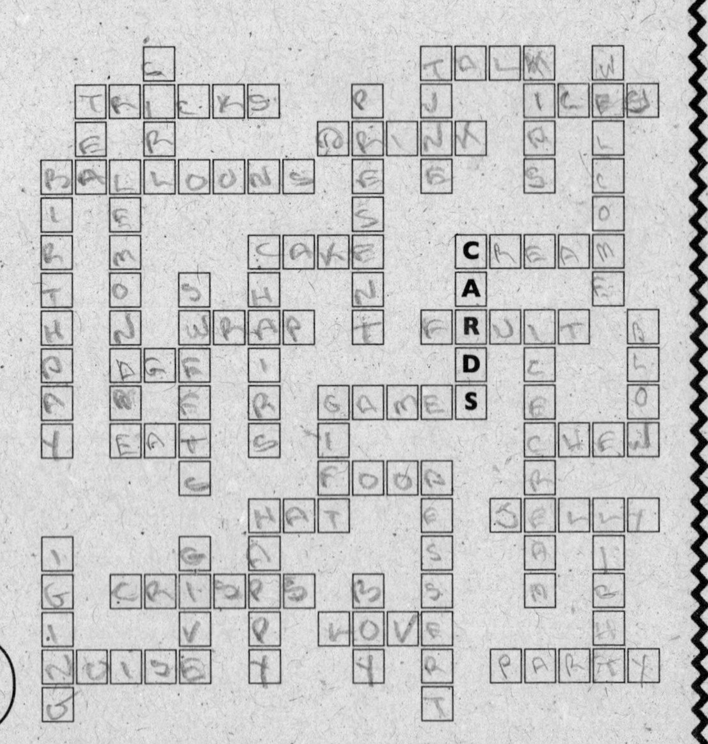

NUMERIC

3 LETTERS
FEW
LOT
LOW
NIL
ONE
SIX
TEN
TWO

4 LETTERS
FOUR
LESS
MANY
MORE
NINE
NONE
ZERO

5 LETTERS
COUNT
EIGHT
FIFTY
SEVEN
THREE
TIMES

6 LETTERS
ELEVEN
NUMBER
TWELVE
TWENTY

7 LETTERS
FIFTEEN
HUNDRED
MILLION
SIXTEEN

8 LETTERS
EIGHTEEN
FOURTEEN
NINETEEN
NUMEROUS
THIRTEEN
THOUSAND

9 LETTERS
SEVENTEEN

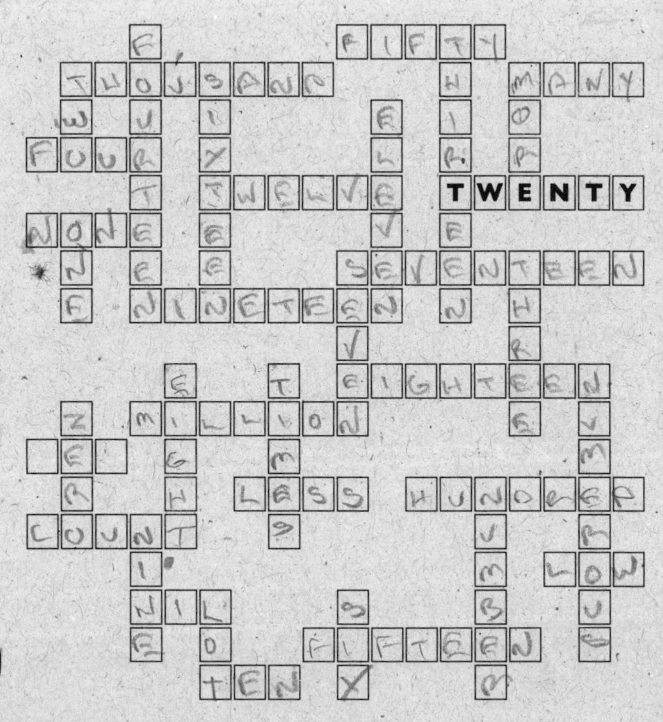

CLANGERS

3 LETTERS
ERR

4 LETTERS
GOOF
SLIP

5 LETTERS
FALSE
FOLLY
GAFFE
WRONG

6 LETTERS
BOOBOO
ERRORS
FAULTY
HOWLER
SLIP-UP
UNFAIR
UNJUST
UNTRUE

7 LETTERS
BLOOMER
BLUNDER
CLANGER
CONFUSE
FAUX PAS
MISLEAD
MISTAKE
NOT TRUE
OFF BEAM

13 LETTERS
MISUNDERSTOOD

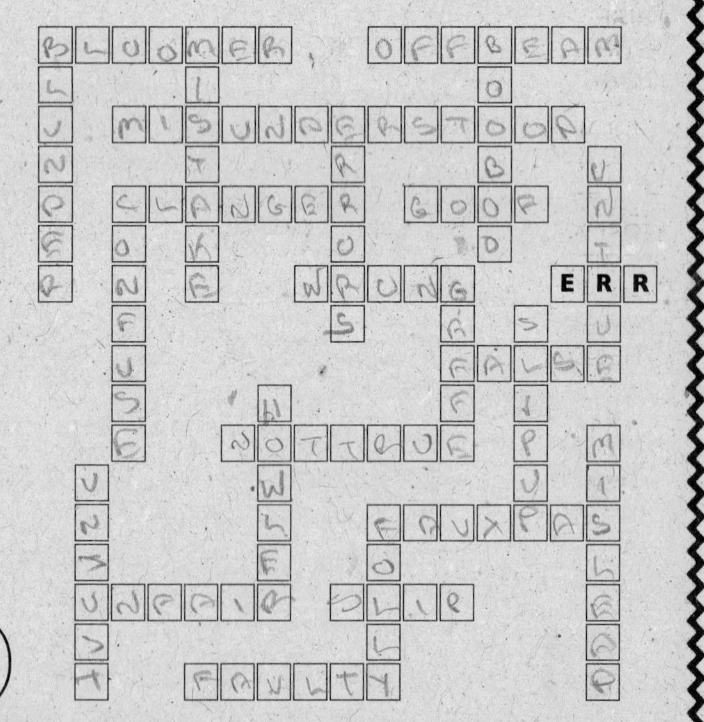

UP'S AND DOWN'S

3 LETTERS
EBB
SIT

4 LETTERS
CAVE
ECHO
FEES
HEAT
HILL
HOPE
JUMP
KITE
LARK
LEAD
LIFT
MAST
RISE
STIR
TONE

5 LETTERS
ALOFT
DOUBT
EPSOM
ORBIT
PITCH
TOWER
TREND

6 LETTERS
AMOUNT
DAUBER
DEFEAT
DETOUR
FLIGHT
GRADES
IDEALS
LADDER
PRICES
REGARD
ROCKET
SKIING
THRUST
TYRANT

7 LETTERS
ANTENNA
EXALTED
FRESHEN
INCOMES
SKI LIFT
STUMBLE

8 LETTERS
BUSINESS
EYEBROWS
JET PLANE
MOUNTAIN

10 LETTERS
ADJUSTMENT
HELICOPTER

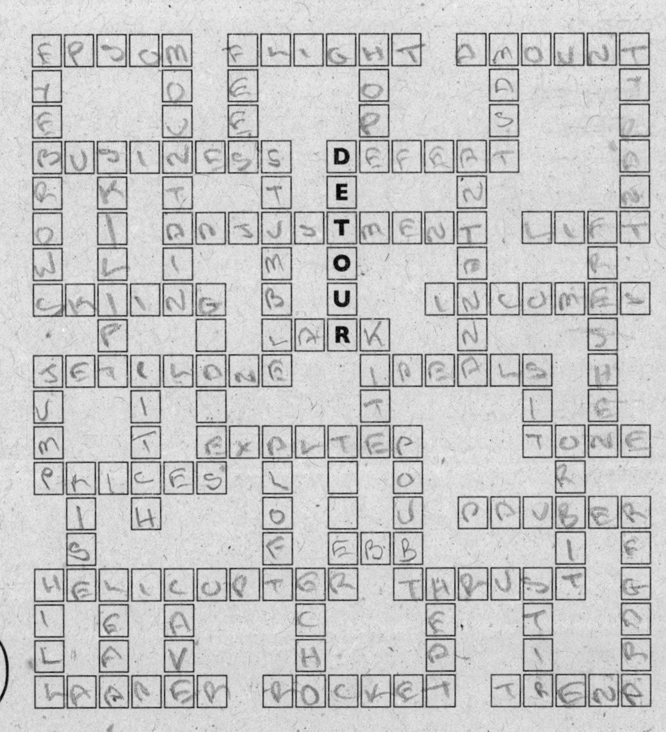

MAPPED OUT

3 LETTERS
BAY
MAP
SEA

4 LETTERS
CAVE
CITY
FARM
LOCH
MERE
MILL
PATH
ROAD
SAND
TOLL

5 LETTERS
ABBEY
BEACH
CREEK
HOUSE
MARSH
MOORS
PARKS
RIVER
SCALE
TRAIL

6 LETTERS
CASTLE
CAVERN
CHURCH
FOREST
GARDEN
ISLAND
MUSEUM
PALACE
RESORT

7 LETTERS
GALLERY
HARBOUR
MINSTER

9 LETTERS
CATHEDRAL
WATERFALL

10 LETTERS
LIGHTHOUSE

G WHIZ

3 LETTERS
GAD
GAG
GAR
GAS
GEE
GIN
GOO
GOT

4 LETTERS
GEAR
GLEE
GNAW
GONG
GREW
GRIN
GROG

5 LETTERS
GAINS
GALES
GAVEL
GHANA
GNARL
GORGE
GRACE
GRAND
GRATE
GRIME

6 LETTERS
GARAGE
GASPED
GATHER
GAUGES
GIVING
GLIDER
GOADER
GORGON
GREASE
GUSTED

7 LETTERS
GAGGING
GARMENT

8 LETTERS
GEORGIAN
GIGGLING
GOINGS ON
GREATEST
GRILLAGE

9 LETTERS
GALVANISE
GARRULOUS
GNOME-LIKE
GRADUATED
GREETINGS

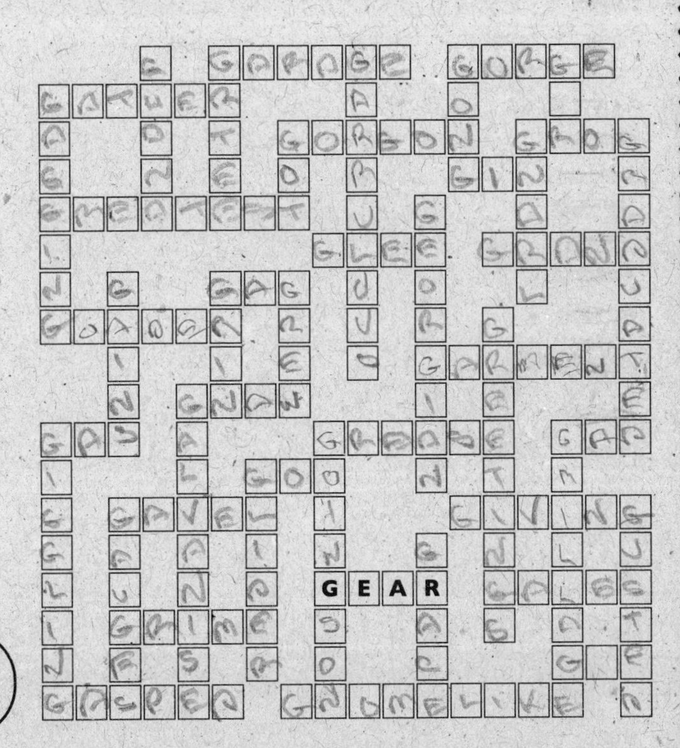

BEAR NECESSITIES

3 LETTERS
DEN
FUR
HUG

4 LETTERS
BABY
COAT
CUBS
CUTE
MALE
PAWS
PLAY
SNOW

5 LETTERS
ADULT
BEARS
BLACK
BROWN
CLAWS
CLIMB
DWELL
HONEY
KOALA
LARGE
POLAR
SLEEP
SMALL
TEDDY
TEETH
WHITE

6 LETTERS
DOZING
FEMALE
FOREST
RUPERT

7 LETTERS
EXPLORE
HABITAT
PLAYFUL
SHELTER
WALKING

9 LETTERS
HIBERNATE
MOUNTAINS

10 LETTERS
PADDINGTON

13 LETTERS
WINNIE THE POOH

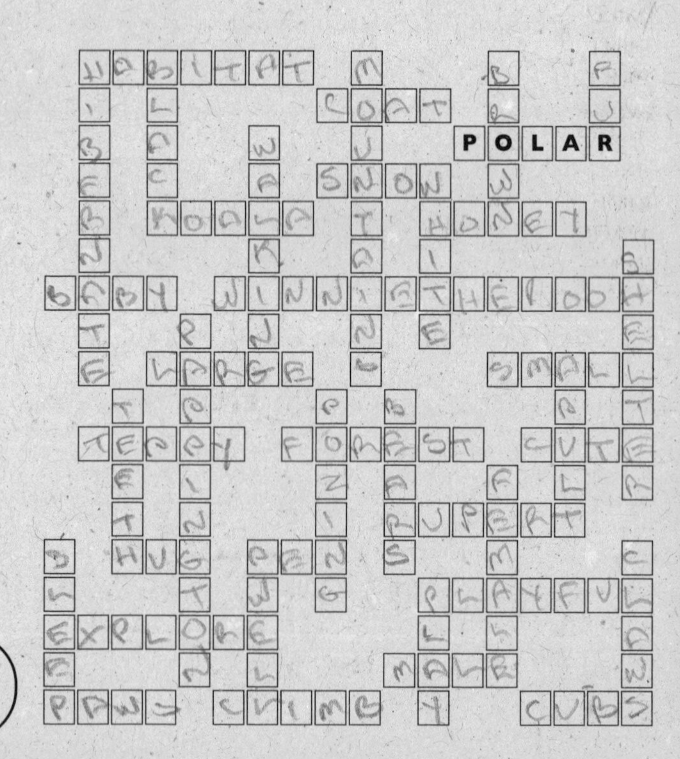

CHEERS!

Take a visit to the local pub.

3 LETTERS
ALE
BAR
EAT
GIN
INN

4 LETTERS
BEER
CHAT
COSY
DINE
FOOD
MENU
MILD
PINT
PULL
PUMP
SNUG
TALK
TIME
WARM
WINE

5 LETTERS
CIDER
DRINK
FROTH
GLASS
LAGER
LOCAL
ROUND
SERVE
STOUT
TABLE
TONIC

6 LETTERS
BITTER
BRANDY
CHAIRS
CHEERS
COFFEE
SHANDY
SHERRY

7 LETTERS
PINK GIN
SPIRITS
VILLAGE

10 LETTERS
REFRESHING

CHEERS

SHOPPING TRIP

3 LETTERS
BUY
TEA

4 LETTERS
BAGS
BELL
CASH
CHAT
FOOD
HELP
OPEN
PAYS
SELL
WRAP

5 LETTERS
BACON
BREAD
CAKES
DRINK
GOODS
MONEY
OFFER
PRICE
SERVE
SHELF
SUGAR

6 LETTERS
ADVICE
BUTTER
CHANGE
CHEESE
CLOSED
SCALES
SLICER
SWEETS
TALKED

7 LETTERS
COUNTER
SERVICE
WEIGHTS

8 LETTERS
CUSTOMER
PURCHASE

10 LETTERS
CORNER SHOP
NEWSPAPERS

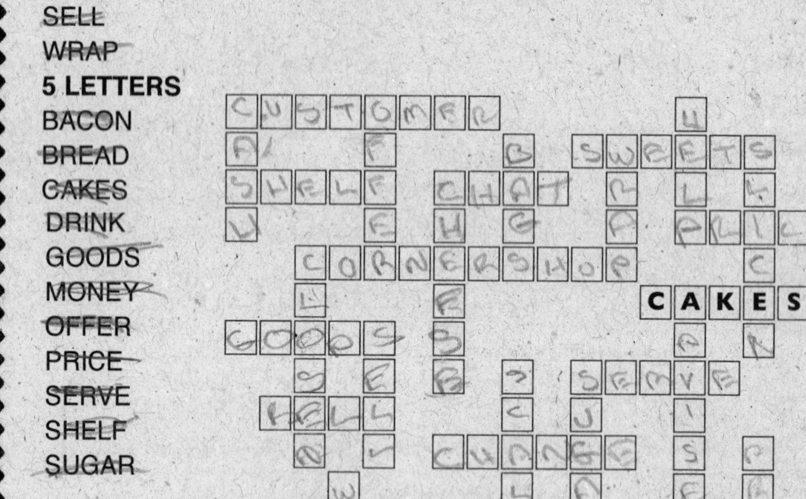

CAR PARTS

3 LETTERS
CAR
FAN
KEY
OIL
TOP

4 LETTERS
BELT
BOOT
DOOR
GEAR
MATS
RIDE
SEAT
STOP

5 LETTERS
CHOKE
FIRST
PLUGS
RADIO
ROADS
SPEED
START
TYRES
WHEEL

6 LETTERS
BONNET
BRAKES
CLUTCH
DRIVER
ENGINE
GARAGE
LIGHTS
PETROL
SECOND
TRAVEL
WIPERS

7 LETTERS
NEUTRAL
REVERSE

8 LETTERS
RADIATOR
ROTOR ARM

9 LETTERS
DASHBOARD
INDICATOR

10 LETTERS
WINDSCREEN

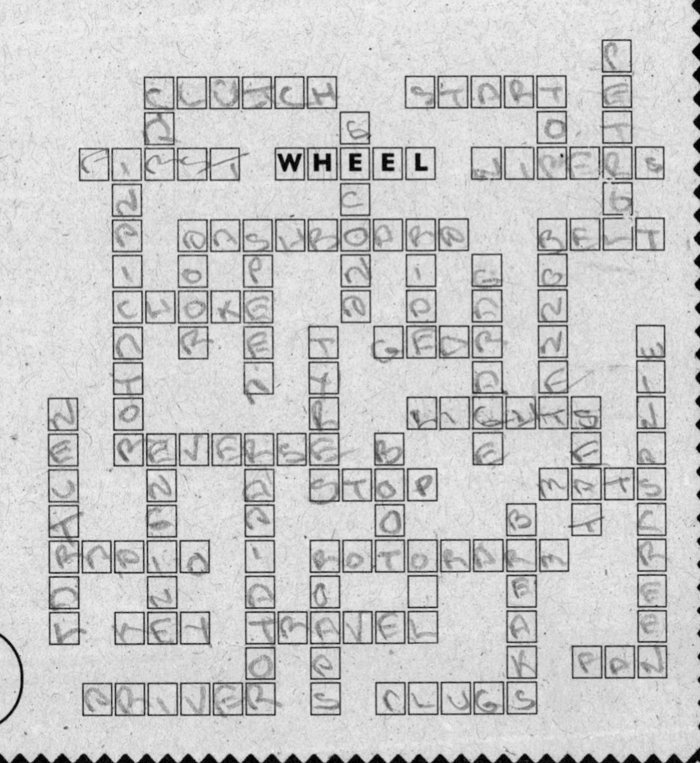

TOP SPOT

4 LETTERS
COST
DEAL
HEAD
NEWS
REAP
SPOT
STAR
SURE
TACT
TEAM
TOPS

5 LETTERS
ASSET
BONUS
CROWN
ECLAT
ELITE
EXCEL
FORCE
GREAT
POISE
SAFER
TITLE
TRAIN
WORTH

6 LETTERS
AWARDS
CAREER
CREDIT
ESTATE
OFFICE
PRAISE
RICHES
STATUS
WEALTH

7 LETTERS
EXALTED
FORTUNE
JACKPOT
RESPECT
SUCCESS
TRIBUTE

8 LETTERS
EMINENCE
POSITION
PROPERTY
SECURITY

9 LETTERS
AFFLUENCE
INFLUENCE

10 LETTERS
CELEBRATED
PROSPERITY
REPUTATION

11 LETTERS
ACHIEVEMENT
ILLUSTRIOUS

BOAT SHOW

3 LETTERS
ARK
TUG

4 LETTERS
BOAT
DHOW
DORY
PUNT
RAFT
SCOW
SHIP
YAWL

5 LETTERS
BARGE
CANOE
COBLE
FERRY
KETCH
LINER
SCULL
SLOOP
SMACK
YACHT

6 LETTERS
BARQUE
CUTTER
DINGHY
TANKER

7 LETTERS
COASTER
CORACLE
GONDOLA
PONTOON
ROWBOAT
STEAMER

8 LETTERS
LIFEBOAT
SCHOONER
TRIMARAN

9 LETTERS
FREIGHTER
MOTORBOAT

G
O
N
D
O
L
A

TOWN HAUL

3 LETTERS
ELY
EYE
USK

4 LETTERS
DEAL
HOLT
HYDE
KIRN
OBAN
SHAP

5 LETTERS
COLNE
ELGIN
FLINT
KELSO
LOUTH
POOLE
TROON

6 LETTERS
BATLEY
BRUTON
CARRON
DUNOON
HENLEY
KENDAL
NEWARK
OUNDLE
REDCAR
THIRSK
TONGUE
WIDNES

7 LETTERS
ANDOVER
BRAEMAR
CHEADLE
HAWORTH
LINCOLN

8 LETTERS
BIDEFORD
GRANTHAM

9 LETTERS
ULVERSTON

10 LETTERS
BARNSTAPLE

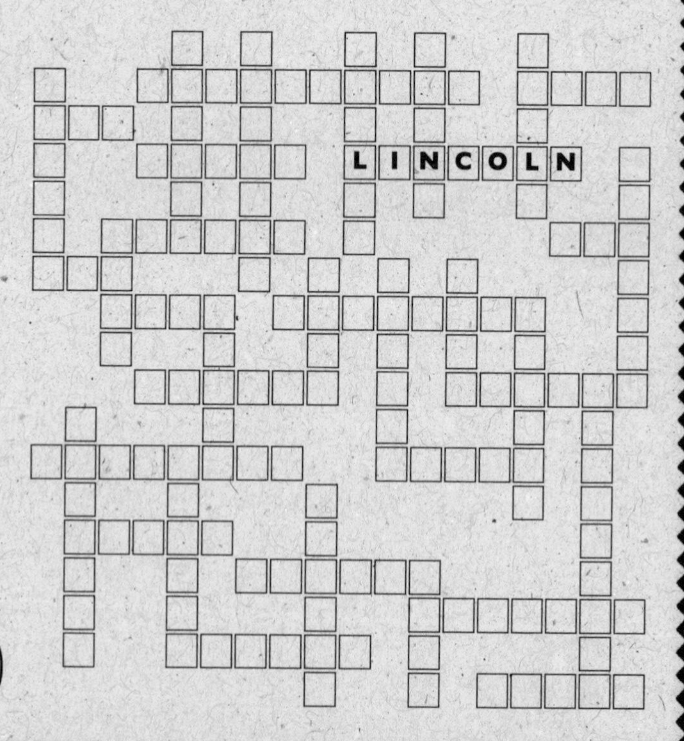

BLIND DATE

Make the perfect match by fitting the words in the grid.

3 LETTERS
HUG
MAN
ONE
TWO
WIN

4 LETTERS
BOYS
KISS
LADS
LOVE
MALE
MEET
PECK
PICK

5 LETTERS
ADORE
CHARM
COURT
GIRLS
ROSES
THREE
WOMAN

6 LETTERS
ANSWER
CHAT UP
CHOOSE
COUPLE
CUDDLE
FEMALE
HUMOUR
LASSES
PRETTY
SCREEN

7 LETTERS
ATTRACT
EMBRACE
PASSION
ROMANCE

8 LETTERS
GORGEOUS
HANDSOME
QUESTION

9 LETTERS
BLIND DATE

10 LETTERS
MATCHMAKER

L A D S

TESTING TIME

3 LETTERS
CAR

4 LETTERS
DOOR
KERB
LANE
LOOK
PASS
SLOW
STOP
TEST
TURN

5 LETTERS
BRAKE
DRIVE
GEARS
LEARN
SIGNS
SPEED
START
STEER
TRAIN
TYRES

6 LETTERS
DRIVER
LIGHTS
MIRROR
SCHOOL
SIGNAL

7 LETTERS
LEARNER
LESSONS
NEUTRAL
REVERSE
TRAFFIC
TUITION

8 LETTERS
EYESIGHT
INSTRUCT

9 LETTERS
HANDBRAKE

10 LETTERS
ROUNDABOUT

11 LETTERS
HIGHWAY CODE

T U I T I O N

CLUELESS

Fit the words in the grid, then make an answer to the clue in the shaded squares.
Shaded clue: Sea creature.

3 LETTERS

IMP
PAN
PEG
TIC

4 LETTERS

AFAR
ASIA
EGGS
ISLE

5 LETTERS

CREPE
PEARL
STICK
SUGAR

6 LETTERS

ANIMAL
LENTIL
RECENT
SUMMER

7 LETTERS

LISSOME
OCTAGON

8 LETTERS

PARTICLE
UNIVERSE

9 LETTERS

TOOTHACHE

TEA TIME

3 LETTERS
HOT
POT
SIP
TEA

4 LETTERS
BOIL
BREW
LEAF
MILD
POUR
STIR
WEAK

5 LETTERS
BLEND
BREAK
CHINA
CREAM
CUPPA
PLANT
SPOON
STEAM
TASTE
WATER

6 LETTERS
BREWED
HERBAL
KETTLE
SAUCER
SOOTHE
TASTED
TEAPOT

7 LETTERS
FLAVOUR
REFRESH
TEA BAGS

8 LETTERS
BEVERAGE
STRAINER

9 LETTERS
SWEETENER

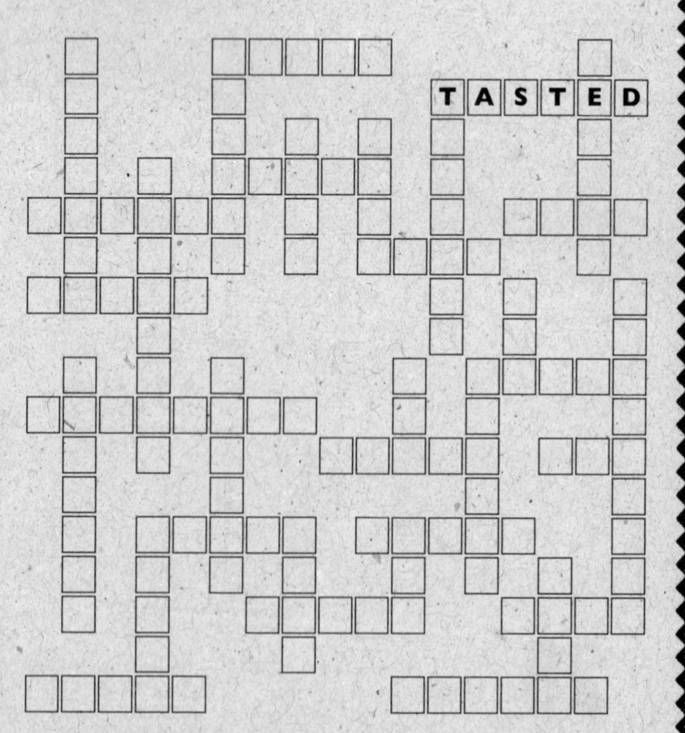

TUNE IN

3 LETTERS
SEE

4 LETTERS
BEAM
DISH
EMIT
HEAR
LOOK
LOUD
PLUG
SOFT
TONE
TUBE

5 LETTERS
CLEAR
FOCUS
RADIO
RANGE
SHARP
SHORT
SOUND
WATCH
WAVES

6 LETTERS
ADJUST
AERIAL
BUTTON
COLOUR
LISTEN
SCREEN
SWITCH
VOLUME

7 LETTERS
CHANNEL
CONTROL
PICTURE
STATION

8 LETTERS
CONTRAST
TRANSMIT
WIRELESS

9 LETTERS
PROGRAMME
SATELLITE

10 LETTERS
TELEVISION

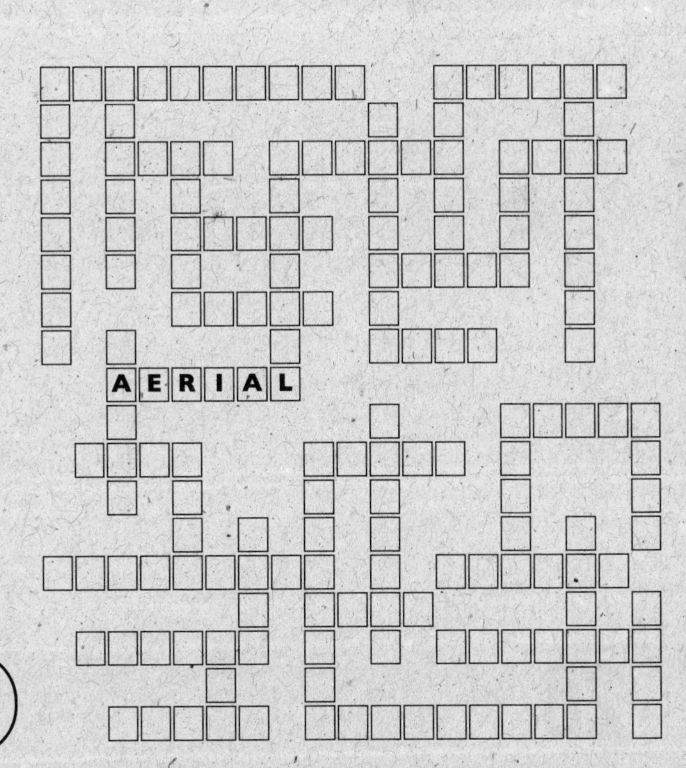

NAMELY

3 LETTERS
JOE
JOY
KAY
LEN
LEO

4 LETTERS
JACK
JANE
KATE
LIAM
LUKE

5 LETTERS
JAMES
JASON
JULIE
KAREN
KEITH
KELLY
LARRY
LAURA
LINDA
LORNA

6 LETTERS
JOLENE
LYNDON

7 LETTERS
JESSICA
LARISSA
LEONARD
LEONORA

8 LETTERS
LORRAINE

9 LETTERS
JOSEPHINE
KATHERINE

10 LETTERS
JACQUELINE

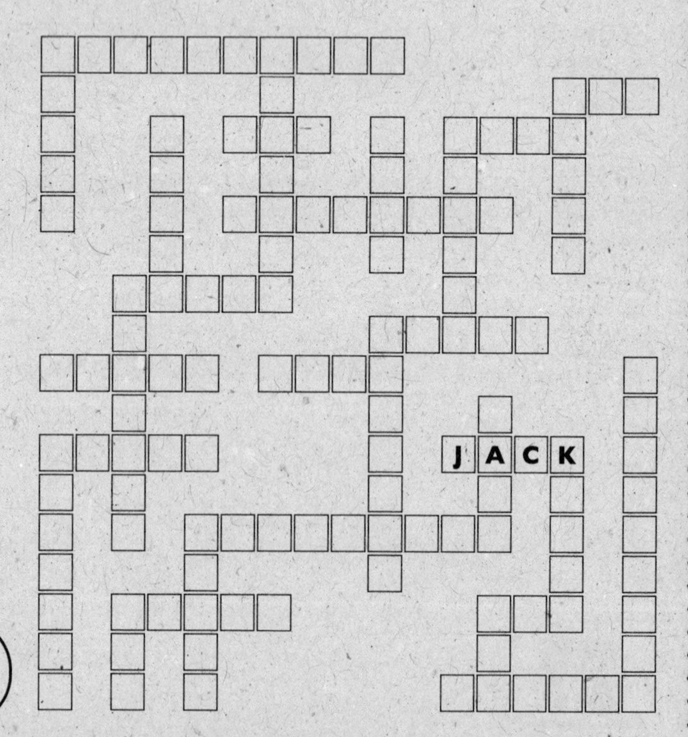

CARD SHARP

Shuffle the words into the grid.

3 LETTERS
ACE
RED
RUN
WIN

4 LETTERS
BEAT
CLUB
DEAL
GAME
HAND
JACK
KING
LAID
LEAD
SNAP
SUIT
TURN

5 LETTERS
BLACK
CARDS
COURT
DEUCE
HEART
JOKER
SPADE
STICK
TRUMP
TWIST
WHIST

6 LETTERS
BRIDGE
DEALER
PLAYER

7 LETTERS
CANASTA
DIAMOND
DISCARD
PONTOON
SHUFFLE

8 LETTERS
BACCARAT
CRIBBAGE
PATIENCE

9 LETTERS
FULL HOUSE

10 LETTERS
ROYAL FLUSH

ARTISTIC

3 LETTERS
ART
INK
PEN

4 LETTERS
DARK
DRAW
FAST
FORM
LEAD
MOVE
TONE

5 LETTERS
ERASE
LIGHT
LINES
PAPER
SCALE
SHADE
SKILL
STYLE
WORDS

6 LETTERS
ANIMAL
ARTIST
DETAIL
FIGURE
PAINTS
PENCIL
SKETCH
SMOOTH
TALENT

7 LETTERS
ANIMATE
CARTOON
COLOURS

8 LETTERS
FREEHAND
LIFELIKE

9 LETTERS
ANIMATION

10 LETTERS
CARTOONIST

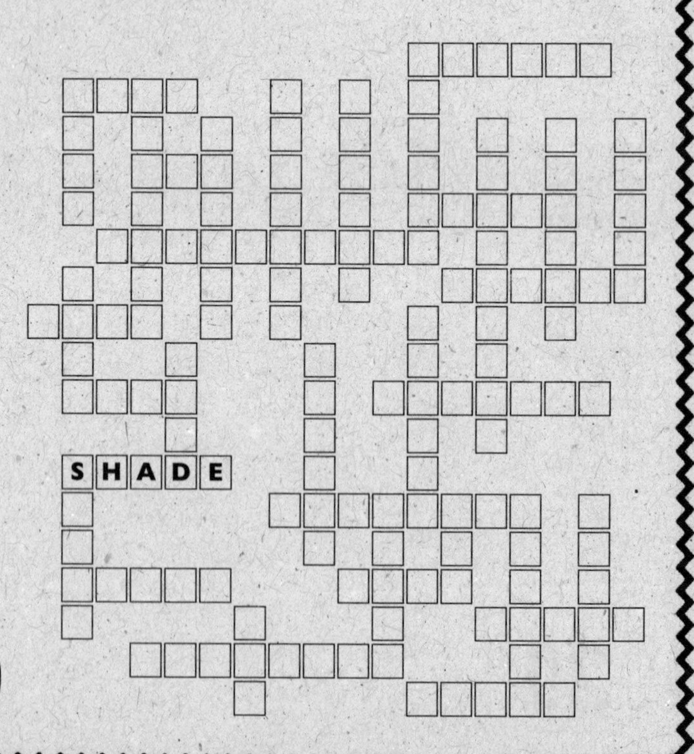

WEATHER REPORT

3 LETTERS
AIR
DRY
END
HOT
ICE
ICY
LOW
SUN

4 LETTERS
CALM
DULL
GUST
HEAT
MIST
RISE
ROAR
SNOW
VEER
WARM
WEST
WILD

5 LETTERS
CIRRI
LEAST
SHINE
SLATY
UNFIT
WINDY

6 LETTERS
BRIGHT
HEAVEN
RANDOM
SQUALL
WINTER
ZEPHYR

7 LETTERS
BRACING
DRIZZLE
RAVAGED
STRATUS
SUNSPOT
TEMPEST
THERMAL
TORNADO

8 LETTERS
DOWNPOUR
OVERCAST

S U N

TALKING WET

3 LETTERS
DIP
GOO
HIP
HOT
ICE
SEA
SOP
SOW

4 LETTERS
ARCH
CLAP
COLD
DASH
DRIP
EVIL
ISLE

5 LETTERS
BASIN
DIKES
FLASH
FLOOD
GULLY
MISTS
ROLLS
SLIDE
SLUSH
STORM

6 LETTERS
ONRUSH
PARKAS
PISCES
PUDDLE
RIPPLE
SPLASH
SPRING
STREAM

7 LETTERS
ARCTICS
DANGERS
FRESHET
OILSKIN
RINSING
SLICKER
SPATTER
SPLOTCH
THUNDER

8 LETTERS
DOWNPOUR
GALOSHES
SPLATTER
SPRINKLE

9 LETTERS
LIGHTNING
RAINDROPS
UNSETTLED

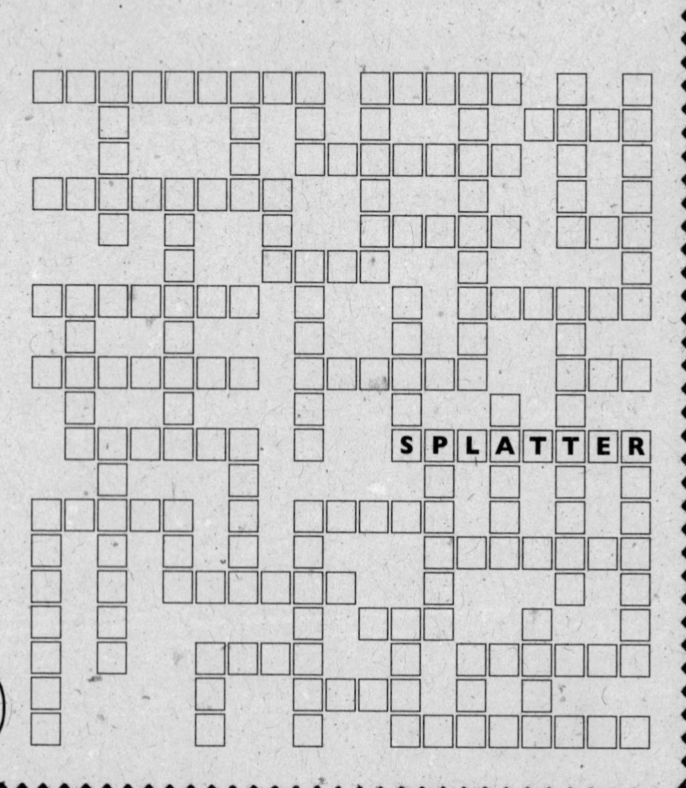

ON THE THAMES

3 LETTERS
EBB
LOW

4 LETTERS
BANK
BEND
BOAT
CALM
ETON
FLOW
HIGH
LOCK
MOVE
RISE
RUNS
TOWN
WIND

5 LETTERS
BROAD
FALLS
MOUTH
RIVER
ROUGH
SHIPS
STILL
SWIFT
TIDES
TOWER
WATER
WAVES

6 LETTERS
BRIDGE
CASTLE
FLOODS
HENLEY
LONDON
MARLOW
OXFORD
RIPPLE
SOURCE
STREAM
THAMES
VALLEY

7 LETTERS
TOWPATH
WINDSOR

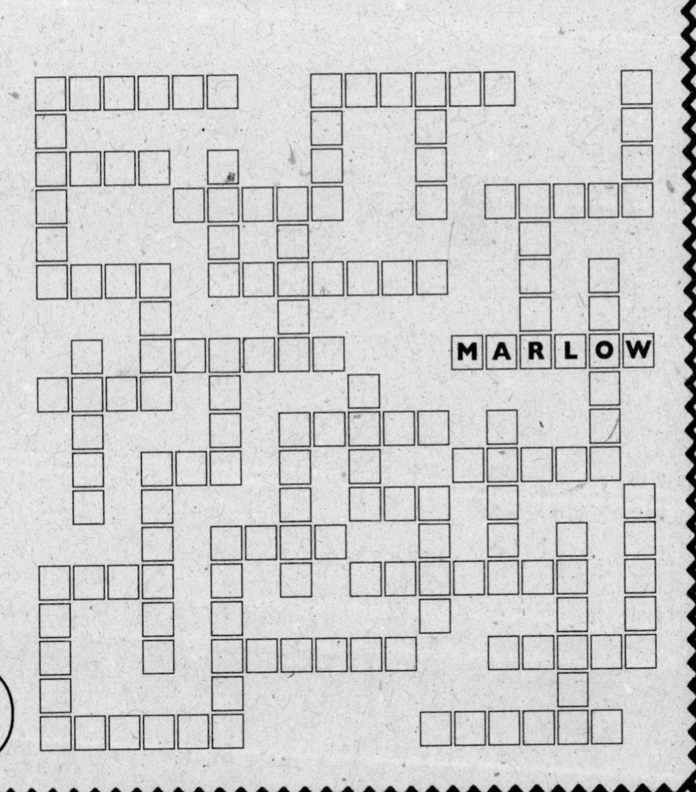

SPOTTED

3 LETTERS
ARC
CAP
EYE
KIT
LAD
SOS

4 LETTERS
ACES
BLOT
CARD
DOTS
HOSE
KILT
MATS
MOLE
MOTH
PIED
PIPS
POGO
RASH
SITE
TOAD

5 LETTERS
CHART
LASER
PINTO
SNAKE
SPOTS
TROUT
TWEED

6 LETTERS
FLECKS
HEARTS
SADDLE
SPECKS
SPIDER
TATTOO

7 LETTERS
DAPPLED
LEOPARD
LIZARDS
MOTTLED

8 LETTERS
CONFETTI
DOMINOES
FRECKLES
INK SPOTS
PEACOCKS
SUNSPOTS

9 LETTERS
DALMATIAN
SPLOTCHES

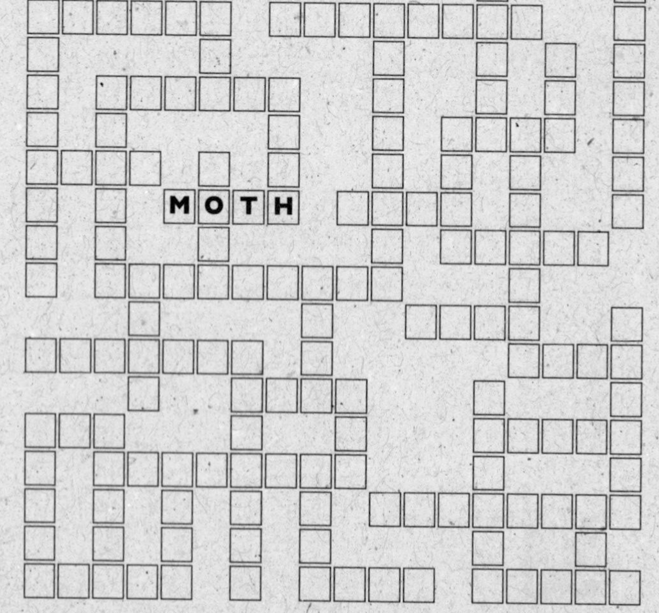

SHOPPING TRIP

3 LETTERS
BAG
BUY
PAY

4 LETTERS
CASH
EGGS
FILL
FOOD
SAVE
SELL
TILL
TINS
WINE

5 LETTERS
AISLE
BRAND
BREAD
DATES
DRINK
GOODS
MONEY
PRICE
SOUPS
STACK
STAFF

6 LETTERS
BASKET
CEREAL
REFUND

7 LETTERS
BARCODE
BOTTLES
PACKETS
PRODUCT
SHOPPER
TROLLEY

8 LETTERS
CHECK-OUT
DISCOUNT
SHOPPING

9 LETTERS
CUSTOMERS

10 LETTERS
VEGETABLES

11 LETTERS
SUPER–MARKET

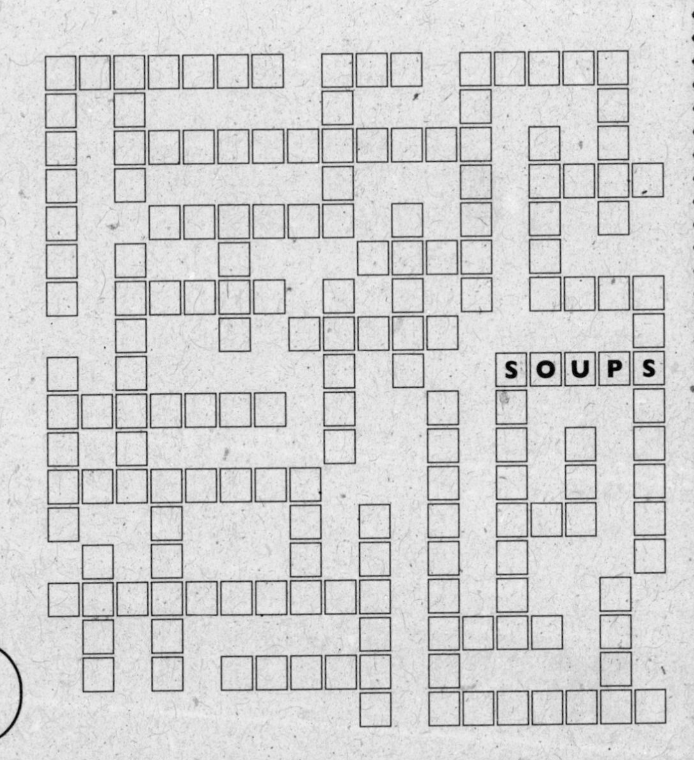

HOMELY

3 LETTERS
BED
MAT
RUG

4 LETTERS
BATH
DOOR
HALL
HOME
LAMP
LINO
LOFT
OVEN
ROOF
SINK
SOFA
TAPS

5 LETTERS
ATTIC
CHAIR
CLOCK
FLOOR
LIGHT
RADIO
ROOMS
STOOL
TABLE
TILES

6 LETTERS
CARPET
LOUNGE
TOILET

7 LETTERS
BEDROOM
KITCHEN

8 LETTERS
UPSTAIRS

9 LETTERS
FIREPLACE
FURNITURE
STAIRCASE

10 LETTERS
DOWNSTAIRS
TELEVISION

T I L E S

LOCKED IN

3 LETTERS
GUM
PIN
SEW
TIE

4 LETTERS
BIND
BOLT
BOND
GLUE
KNIT
MEND
MOOR
NAIL
WELD

5 LETTERS
AFFIX
CHAIN
PASTE
RIVET
STICK
WEDGE

6 LETTERS
ADHERE
ANCHOR
BUTTON
CEMENT
FETTER
REPAIR
SECURE
STAPLE
STITCH
TETHER

7 LETTERS
HARNESS
PADLOCK

8 LETTERS
DOORSTOP

9 LETTERS
FASTENING

10 LETTERS
HOOK AND EYE

11 LETTERS
PAPERWEIGHT

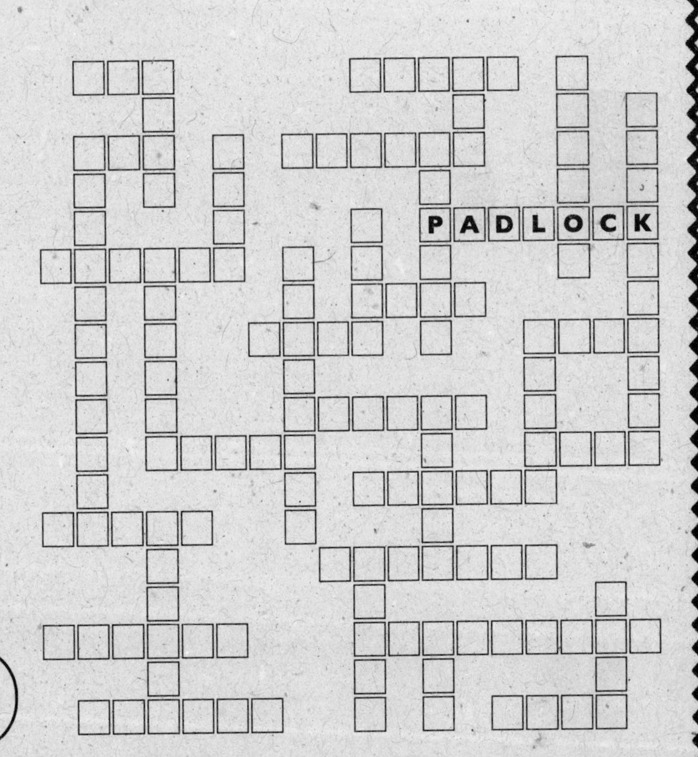

FRYING TONIGHT

3 LETTERS
EGG
OIL
WOK

4 LETTERS
COOK
HEAT
MEAL
OVEN
SALT

5 LETTERS
AROMA
BACON
BURNT
CHIPS
CRISP
FLAME
GRILL
KNIFE
TASTE

6 LETTERS
BATTER
NAPKIN
PEPPER
PLATES
POTATO
SIZZLE
TOMATO

7 LETTERS
CRACKLE
KITCHEN
SAUSAGE
STIR FRY
VINEGAR

8 LETTERS
BARBECUE
MUSHROOM
UTENSILS

10 LETTERS
BEEFBURGER
VEGETABLES

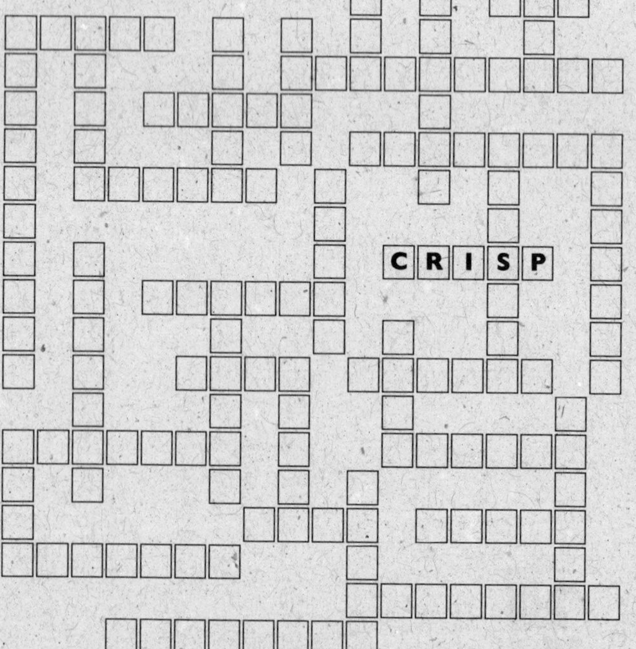

BUGGED

3 LETTERS
ANT
BEE
BUG
COB
FLY

4 LETTERS
FLEA
GNAT
GRUB
MITE
MOTH
NEWT
TICK
WASP

5 LETTERS
APHID
BORER
CIMEX
CULEX
ERUCA
LARVA
LOUSE
MIDGE
VESPA

6 LETTERS
BEETLE
CICADA
EARWIG
HORNET
MAGGOT
SCARAB
SPIDER
TSETSE
WEEVIL

7 LETTERS
CRICKET
FIREFLY
MICROBE
TERMITE

8 LETTERS
LADYBIRD
WOODLICE

9 LETTERS
BUTTERFLY
CENTIPEDE
MILLEPEDE

CAT NAP

3 LETTERS
CAT
FUR
SIT
TOM

4 LETTERS
BOWL
FLAP
FOOD
LEAP
LOVE
MILK
PAWS
PLAY
ROLL
TAIL
TOYS

5 LETTERS
CLAWS
CLEAN
CLIMB
CREAM
DRINK
TABBY
WATCH

6 LETTERS
BASKET
FRIEND
GINGER
KITTEN
LITTER
SPRING

7 LETTERS
LICKING
PERSIAN
PLAYFUL
PURRING
SCRATCH
SIAMESE

8 LETTERS
WHISKERS

11 LETTERS
INTELLIGENT

12 LETTERS
AFFECTIONATE

L I T T E R

POSTAL ORDER

3 LETTERS
BUY
INK
PEN

4 LETTERS
CORD
SHOP
TAGS
TAPE

5 LETTERS
BOOKS
CARDS
FORMS
QUEUE
MONEY
PAPER

6 LETTERS
CRISPS
JOTTER
LETTER
PACKET
PARCEL
PENCIL
RUBBER
STAMPS
STRING
SWEETS

7 LETTERS
AIRMAIL
COUNTER
LICENCE
NOTELET
PENSION
TICKETS

8 LETTERS
ENVELOPE
POSTCARD

10 LETTERS
POST OFFICE
STATIONERY

11 LETTERS
POSTAL ORDER

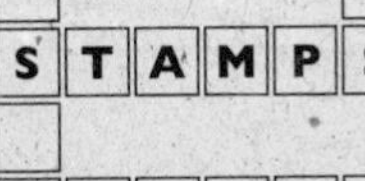
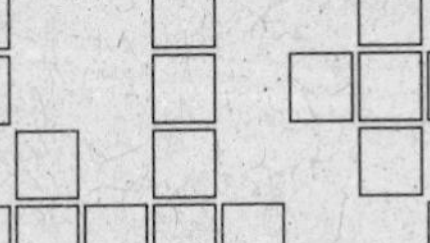
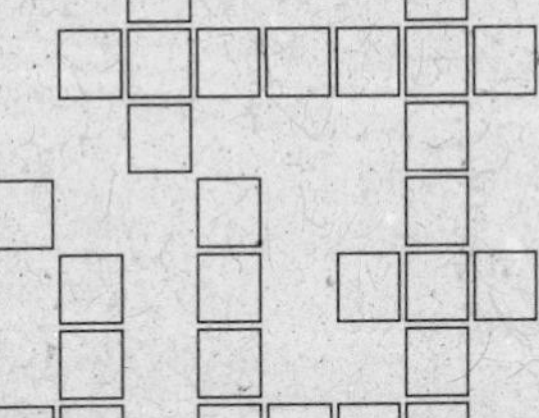

S T A M P S

TAKE OFF

3 LETTERS
AIR
EAT
FAR
FOG

4 LETTERS
CREW
JETS
MILK
SIGN
TIME
TYRE

5 LETTERS
BELTS
CARGO
EARLY
ENTER
LANDS
OCEAN
RADIO
READS
RESTS
ROUGH
SEATS
SKIES
SPEED
TOWER

6 LETTERS
CLOUDS
DRINKS
ENGINE
MOVIES
SLEEPS
SMOOTH
TENSES
TICKET

7 LETTERS
COCKPIT
LUGGAGE
TAKE-OFF
TOURIST
TREMBLE

8 LETTERS
ALTITUDE
AVIATION
DISTANCE
PASSPORT

9 LETTERS
DETENTION
ELEVATION

10 LETTERS
FIRST CLASS
PASSENGERS
STEWARDESS

POTTY

3 LETTERS
DIP
JUG

4 LETTERS
BAKE
BONE
DISH
HEAT
KILN
OVEN
POTS
RACK
SPIN
VASE

5 LETTERS
BOWLS
CHINA
GLAZE
MOULD
PAINT
THROW
WATER
WHEEL

6 LETTERS
COLOUR
ENAMEL
FIRING
HARDEN
SHAPED
TURNER

7 LETTERS
BLENDER
BUBBLES
ENGRAVE
GILDING
POTTERY
WHIRLER

8 LETTERS
DECORATE
ORNAMENT

9 LETTERS
PORCELAIN

11 LETTERS
EARTHENWARE

CLUELESS

Fit the words in the grid, then make an answer to the clue in the shaded squares.

Shaded clue: Sea creature.

3 LETTERS

ARC

BAG

ERA

RUT

4 LETTERS

FEEL

FLEA

RASP

STEP

5 LETTERS

CLIFF

LEGAL

SLATE

SPORT

6 LETTERS

CHALKS

LIGHTS

SEASON

STREET

7 LETTERS

CANASTA

DELIGHT

8 LETTERS

PARASITE

PERSUADE

9 LETTERS

SOUNDLESS

PARTY TIME

3 LETTERS
SIP
SIT

4 LETTERS
BEAT
BEER
FIZZ
OPEN
PLAY
ROMP
SEXY
SPIN

5 LETTERS
BANJO
CLOWN
CRAZE
DANCE
DRINK
ENJOY
EXTRA
FLAIR
FUNNY
GROPE
LOVER
NIFTY
TIPSY
TONIC

6 LETTERS
ASLEEP
CHASER
CHEERS
DEPART
FRIEND
PAIRED
PARADE
SEDUCE
SHERRY
SOCIAL
TIRING
UNRULY

7 LETTERS
BEWITCH
CLAMOUR
ELEGANT
FESTIVE
RELAXED
STILTON

WINE TASTER

3 LETTERS
DRY
RED
SIP
TRY

4 LETTERS
COLD
CORK
FILL
GROW
OPEN
PORT
POUR
TANG
VINE
WINE
YEAR

5 LETTERS
DRINK
FRUIT
GLASS
LABEL
SHARP
SMELL
SWEET
TASTE
TREAD
WHITE

6 LETTERS
BOTTLE
BUBBLY
CELLAR
GRAPES
MATURE
SHERRY
STRONG
UNCORK

7 LETTERS
VINTAGE

8 LETTERS
BURGUNDY
VINEYARD

9 LETTERS
CHAMPAGNE
CORKSCREW
FORTIFIED

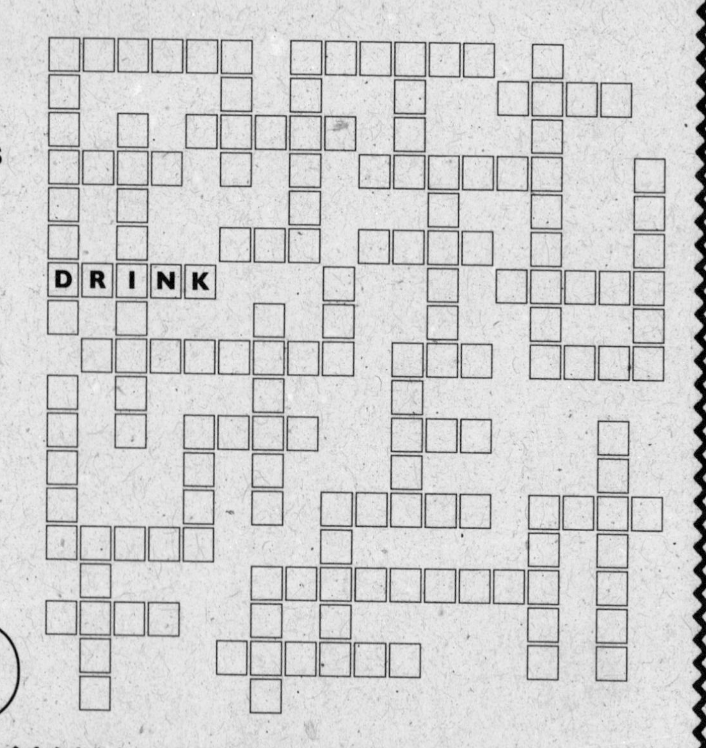

IN HOUSE

3 LETTERS
BAG
FAN
GAS
HOB
PAN
SAW

4 LETTERS
ITEM
JAMB
KNOB
OVEN
PLUG
SOAP
VASE
WIRE

5 LETTERS
APRON
BRASS
DRILL
DUVET
EARTH
FUNGI
GRATE
GUEST
MUSIC
PIANO
SEDAN
TOAST

6 LETTERS
BONNET
COBWEB
CRAVAT
DRY ROT
GARAGE
PLENTY
POLISH

RECIPE
SPICES
SPIDER
SPRING
TEAPOT
TISSUE
WARMTH

7 LETTERS
IRONING
SPATULA
TANKARD
TURMOIL

8 LETTERS
HOTPLATE
SCISSORS

DATE LINE

3 LETTERS
ASK
BOY

4 LETTERS
CHAT
DATE
FOND
GIRL
HOLD
KISS
LADY
MATE
MEET
RING
TALK
TALL
WARM

5 LETTERS
ALONE
CARED
HEART
LOVES
PHONE
ROMEO
SHORT

6 LETTERS
FEMALE
FRIEND
HUMOUR
LONELY

7 LETTERS
COMPANY
EMBRACE
GENUINE
HONESTY
MEETING
SINCERE

8 LETTERS
RELIABLE
ROMANTIC
TOGETHER

9 LETTERS
GENTLEMAN
INTERESTS

BE PATIENT

Fit the hospital words into the grid.

3 LETTERS
BED
ILL

4 LETTERS
ACHE
DOSE
EASE
LAID
SICK
WELL

5 LETTERS
ANGEL
CHEST
DRINK
MEALS
NURSE
PILLS
SCANS
TESTS
TREAT

6 LETTERS
BETTER
DOCTOR
HEALTH
MATRON
PILLOW
SHEETS
UNWELL

7 LETTERS
CURTAIN
PATIENT
PLASTER
SYMPTOM
TABLETS
THEATRE

8 LETTERS
DIAGNOSE
EXAMINED
HOSPITAL
MEDICINE

9 LETTERS
AMBULANCE
OPERATION

A N G E L

MAKING CONTACT

3 LETTERS
FAX
S.O.S.
WEB

4 LETTERS
CALL
CARD
CHAT
MAIL
NEWS
NOTE
POST
TALK
TAPE

5 LETTERS
E-MAIL
SPEAK
TELEX
WRITE

6 LETTERS
NOTICE
REPORT

7 LETTERS
CONTACT
LETTERS

8 LETTERS
INTERNET
POSTCARD
TELEGRAM
TELETEXT

9 LETTERS
BROADCAST
SEMAPHORE
TELEPHONE

11 LETTERS
MOBILE PHONE
TYPEWRITERS
WRITTEN WORD

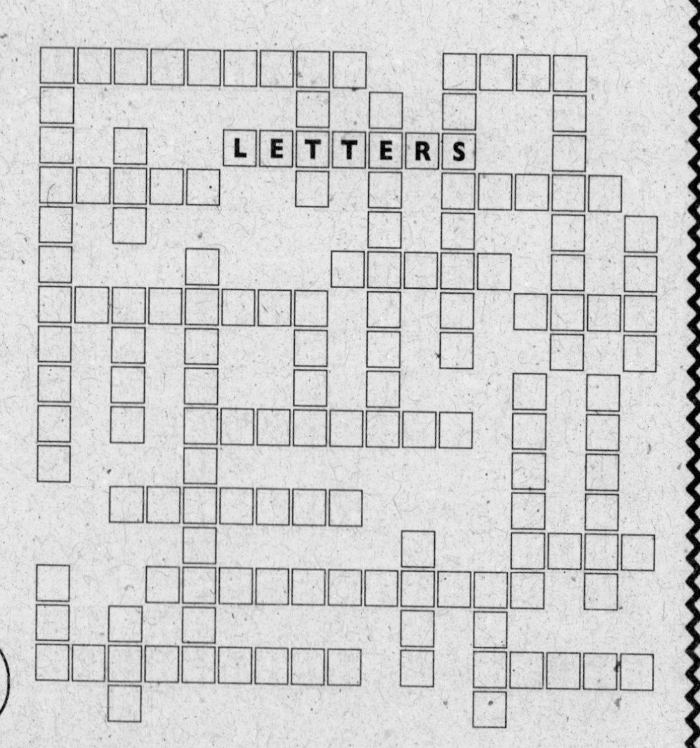

WILD THING

3 LETTERS
BAT
DOE
ELK
GNU
KID
NAG
PET
PUG
RAT
YAK

4 LETTERS
BULL
GOAT
HARE
HART
LAMB
MINK
MULE
ORYX
PUMA
SEAL
STAG
VOLE

5 LETTERS
ADDAX
BEAST
DINGO
ELAND
HIPPO
HORSE
HOUND
HYENA
LLAMA
MOOSE
MOUSE
OKAPI
OTTER
PANDA
RHINO
SKUNK
SWINE
TAPIR
TIGER
WHELP

6 LETTERS
DONKEY
KITTEN

7 LETTERS
BUFFALO
DOLPHIN
LIONESS
PANTHER

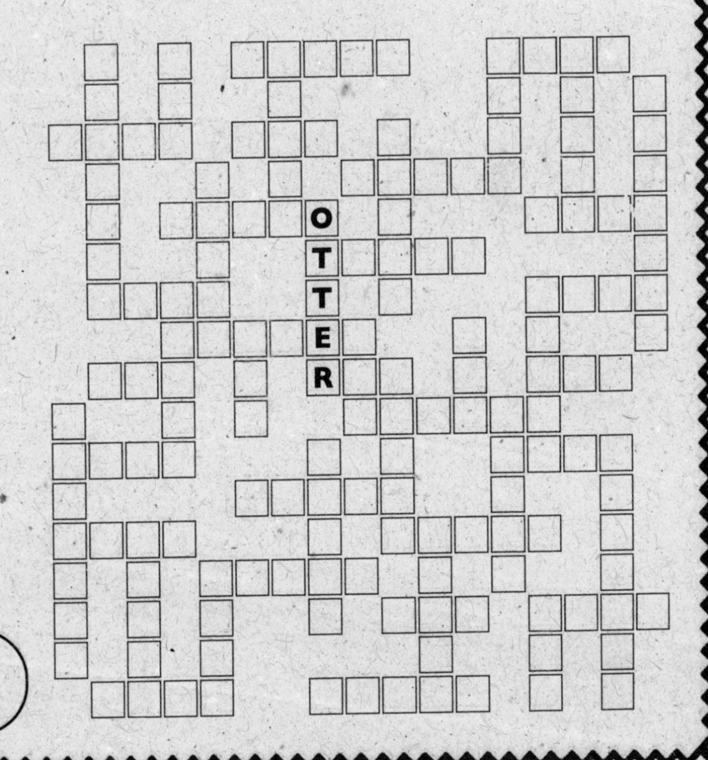

WELL READ

3 LETTERS
ART
SET
OLD

4 LETTERS
BOOK
DATE
FAIR
GILT
LEAF
LIST
RARE
READ
TEXT

5 LETTERS
BOUND
COVER
FIRST
INDEX
ISSUE
PAGES
PLATE
SPINE
TITLE
VALUE

6 LETTERS
AUTHOR
DEALER
JACKET
LEAVES
LONDON
SECOND
SIGNED
STANDS
VOLUME

7 LETTERS
BINDING
EDITION
PRINTED
REPRINT

8 LETTERS
ORIGINAL
SKETCHES

10 LETTERS
LITERATURE

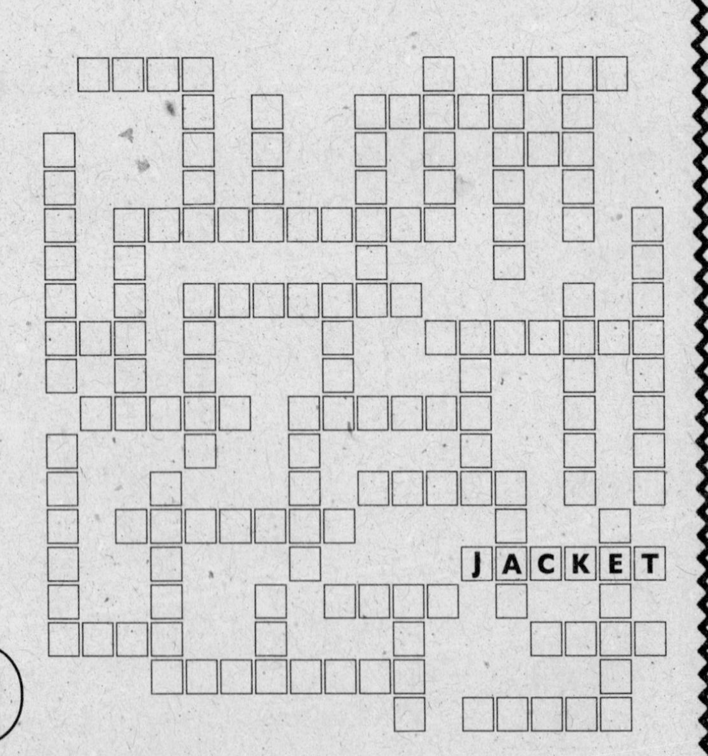

WHAT A RACKET

Fit the words into the grid associated with the Wimbledon tournament.

3 LETTERS
ACE
LET
LOB
MEN
NET
SET

4 LETTERS
BALL
GAME
LAWN
LOVE
PLAY

5 LETTERS
GRASS
LINES
MATCH
MIXED

SCORE
SERVE
SLICE
SMASH

6 LETTERS
COVERS
LADIES
RACKET
RETURN
SERVER
TENNIS
UMPIRE
WINNER

7 LETTERS
DOUBLES
SINGLES
TOP SPIN

8 LETTERS
BACKHAND
FOREHAND

9 LETTERS
ADVANTAGE
FORTNIGHT
VOLLEYING
WIMBLEDON

10 LETTERS
TIE-BREAKER

11 LETTERS
CENTRE COURT

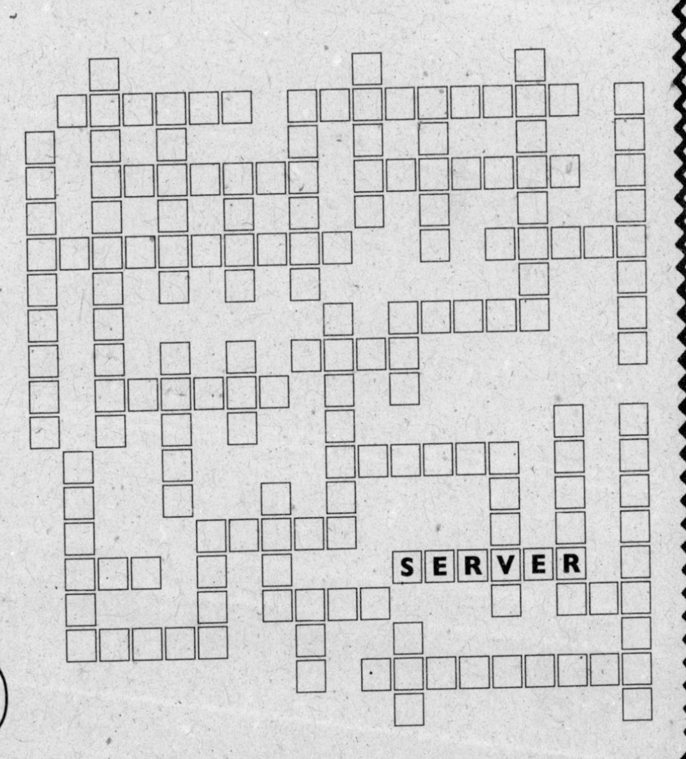

AT THE LOCAL

Can you fit the words into the grid without getting thirsty?

3 LETTERS
ALE
MAT

4 LETTERS
BEER
BREW
FOOD
KIDS
MEAL
PLAY
PULL
SALE

5 LETTERS
DARTS
DRINK
GLASS
LAGER
LOCAL
ROUND
SERVE
WINES

6 LETTERS
BARMAN
BOTTLE
BRANDY
CHAIRS
CHEERS
LOUNGE
ORANGE
SHANDY
SHERRY
TABLES
WHISKY

7 LETTERS
BARMAID
CHATTER
COMPANY
SPIRITS

8 LETTERS
DOMINOES

10 LETTERS
LAST ORDERS

11 LETTERS
OPENING TIME

12 LETTERS
CONVERSATION

B O T T L E

CAR PARTS

3 LETTERS
CAR
FAN
KEY
OIL
TOP

4 LETTERS
BELT
BOOT
DOOR
GEAR
MATS
RIDE
SEAT
STOP

5 LETTERS
CHOKE
FIRST
PLUGS
RADIO
ROADS
SPEED
START
TYRES
WHEEL

6 LETTERS
BONNET
BRAKES
CLUTCH
DRIVER
ENGINE
GARAGE
LIGHTS
PETROL
SECOND
TRAVEL
WIPERS

7 LETTERS
NEUTRAL
REVERSE

8 LETTERS
RADIATOR
ROTOR ARM

9 LETTERS
DASHBOARD
INDICATOR

10 LETTERS
WINDSCREEN

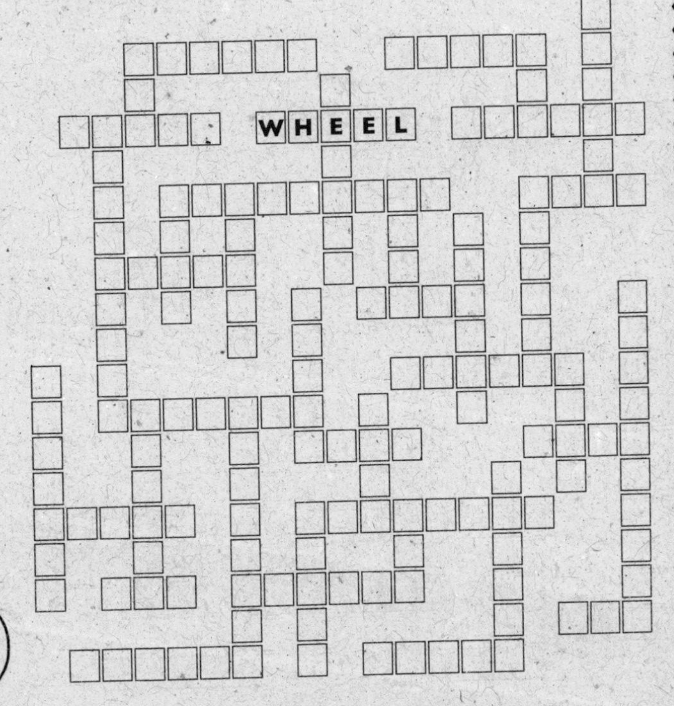

HOLD EVERYTHING

3 LETTERS
BAG
CAN
CUP
JUG
TUB
VAT

4 LETTERS
BINS
BUTT
CASK
CELL
CRIB
GRIP
HOLE
JARS
KEGS
PAIL
SKEP
VASE
VIAL

5 LETTERS
CHEST
CREEL
CRUET
EWERS
FLASK
GLASS
SCRIP
STOUP

6 LETTERS
BARREL
BASINS
BUCKET
CARAFE
CRADLE
FLAGON
NICHES
NOGGIN
RECESS
TEAPOT
VALISE

7 LETTERS
ALEMBIC
AMPHORA
CASTERS
HAMPERS
PANNIER
PATELLA
SOCKETS
UTENSIL
VESSELS

8 LETTERS
SAUCEPAN
SCABBARD

9 LETTERS
DEMIJOHNS

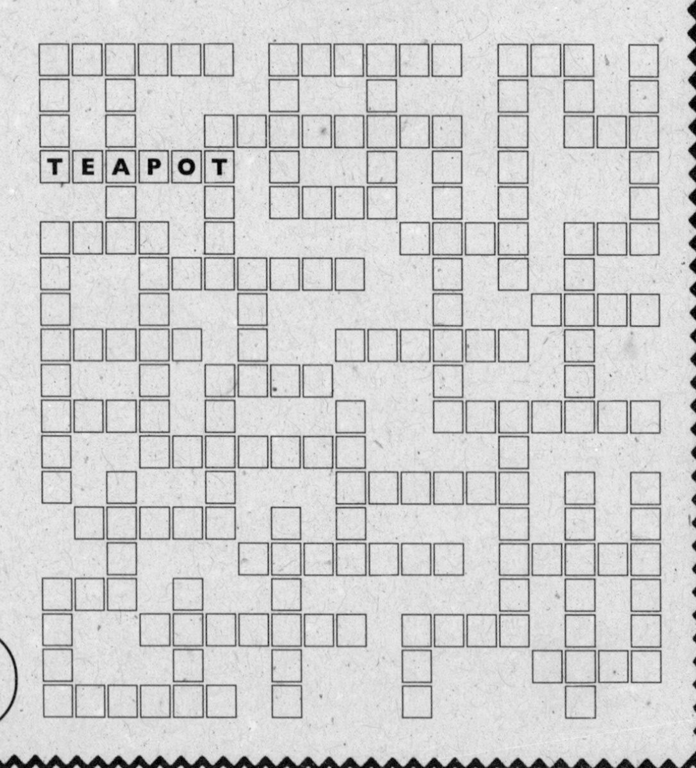

BATH TIME

3 LETTERS
HOT
MAT
TUB
WET

4 LETTERS
BATH
COLD
LAZE
SINK
SOAK
SOAP
TALC
TAPS
WASH

5 LETTERS
CLEAN
DUCKS
RELAX
RINSE
SCRUB
SHAVE
WATER

6 LETTERS
MIRROR
SCALES
SHOWER
SPLASH
SPONGE
TOWELS

7 LETTERS
BUBBLES
FLANNEL
SHAMPOO

8 LETTERS
RADIATOR

10 LETTERS
BRUSH TEETH

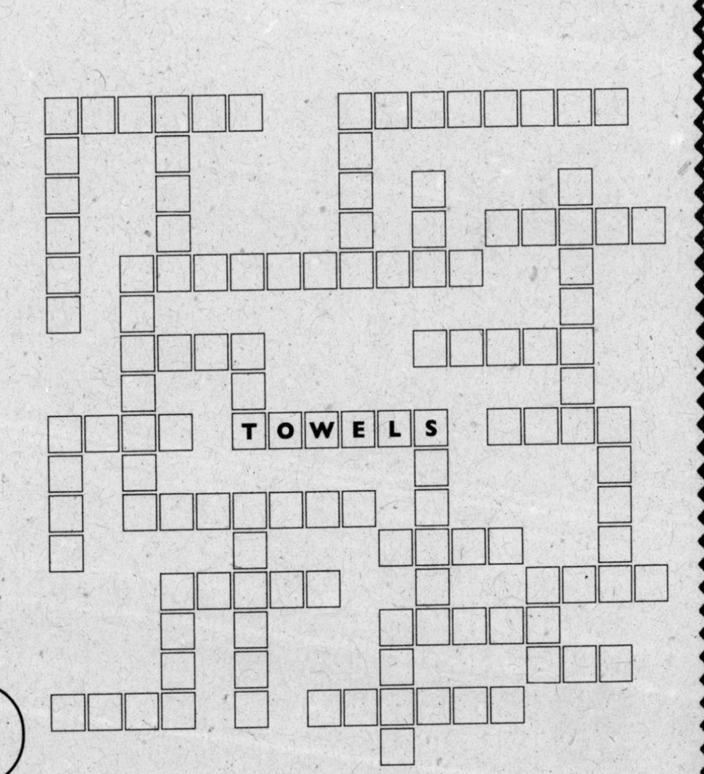

CLUELESS

Fit the words in the grid, then make an answer to the clue in the shaded squares.
Shaded clue: Item of clothing.

4 LETTERS
ACRE
HARP
PEAR
ROAD
TAME
TROT

5 LETTERS
AGATE
DELAY
FINER
FORGE
PLANT
YEAST

6 LETTERS
ADVERT
DEARER
HEROIC
RENTED
TABLET
TEASER

7 LETTERS
ADDICTS
HAMSTER
LEARNER
SALVAGE

8 LETTERS
BLOOMING
GRADIENT

9 LETTERS
AUTHORESS
REPARTEES

10 LETTERS
MICROSCOPE
NAVIGATION

11 LETTERS
GREENHOUSES

LOG ON

2 LETTERS
ON

3 LETTERS
JOB
KEY
RUN
TAB

4 LETTERS
BYTE
EXIT
SAVE
SCAN
TYPE

5 LETTERS
DISCS
DRIVE
ENTER
LOG-ON
MODEM
PIXEL

6 LETTERS
ERRORS
FLOPPY
MEMORY
RELOAD
SCREEN

7 LETTERS
CIRCUIT
HACKING
MONITOR
PROCESS
PROGRAM
SYMBOLS

8 LETTERS
COMPUTER
DOWNLOAD
HARDWARE
PASSWORD
SOFTWARE

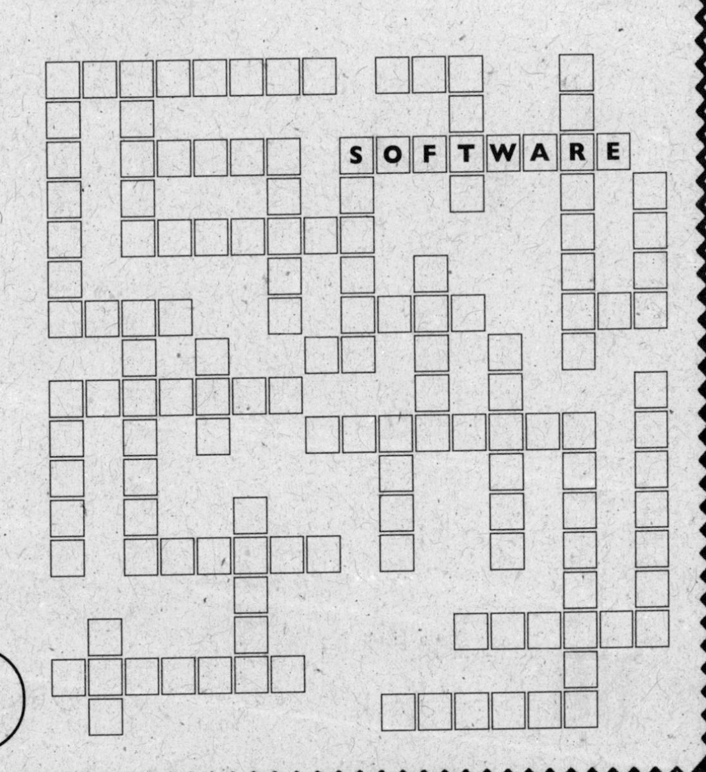

LITTLE THINGS

3 LETTERS
ANT
BEE
FLY

4 LETTERS
FLEA
GNAT
GRUB
MITE
MOTH
WASP
WORM

5 LETTERS
APHID
BORER
DRONE
LOUSE
VESPA

6 LETTERS
BEETLE
CICADA
EARWIG
HORNET
LOCUST
MANTIS
SCARAB
SPIDER
WEEVIL

7 LETTERS
CRICKET
FIREFLY
KATYDID
TERMITE

8 LETTERS
LADYBIRD

9 LETTERS
BUTTERFLY
CENTIPEDE
TSETSE FLY

11 LETTERS
GRASSHOPPER

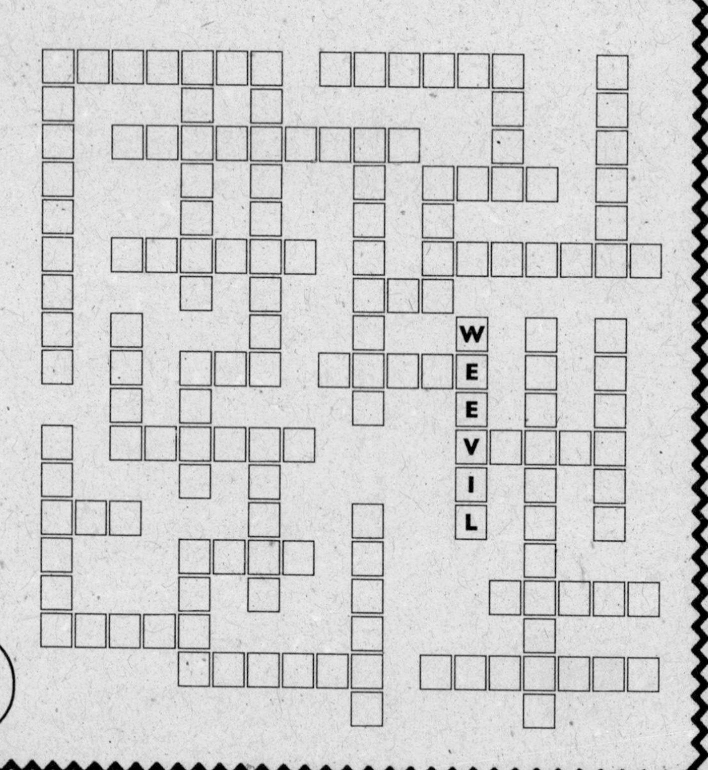

ROYAL GALA

3 LETTERS
ANN
EVE
HAL
IDA
ILE
MEG
ROY

4 LETTERS
ARMS
BESS
DUKE
EMIR
HERO
JOHN
JUAN
KARL
MARY
NIBS
NINA
OTTO
PAUL
PEER
SHAH
THOR
TSAR

5 LETTERS
DAVID
GRACE
HAILE
HELEN
HENRY
NOBLE
URBAN
UTHER

6 LETTERS
EMPIRE
ESTHER
GENTLE
HAMLET
HAROLD
JOSEPH
PHILIP
REGENT
SQUIRE
SULTAN

7 LETTERS
DAUPHIN
DUCHIES
HORATIO
SOLOMON
WINDSOR

8 LETTERS
AGHA KHAN
HAPSBURG
HIGHNESS
NICHOLAS

9 LETTERS
ELIZABETH
ROYALISTS

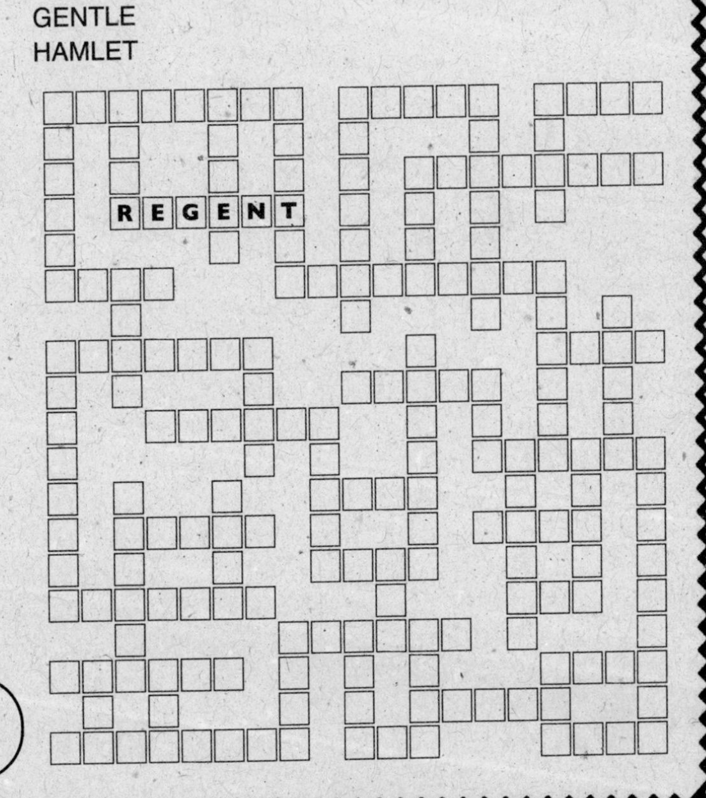

IN THE NEWS

3 LETTERS
DIY
INK

4 LETTERS
EDIT
HOME
LAST
LATE
LOOK
NEWS
READ
TEXT
TYPE

5 LETTERS
EXTRA
FACTS
FIRST
ISSUE
PAGES
PAPER
PRINT
SCOOP
SPORT
STORY
VIEWS

6 LETTERS
EDITOR
FAMILY
HEALTH
TRAVEL

7 LETTERS
ADVERTS
EDITION
FASHION
FEATURE
LETTERS
READERS
WEATHER

8 LETTERS
BUSINESS
REPORTER

9 LETTERS
HEADLINES
NEWSPAPER

10 LETTERS
SUPPLEMENT

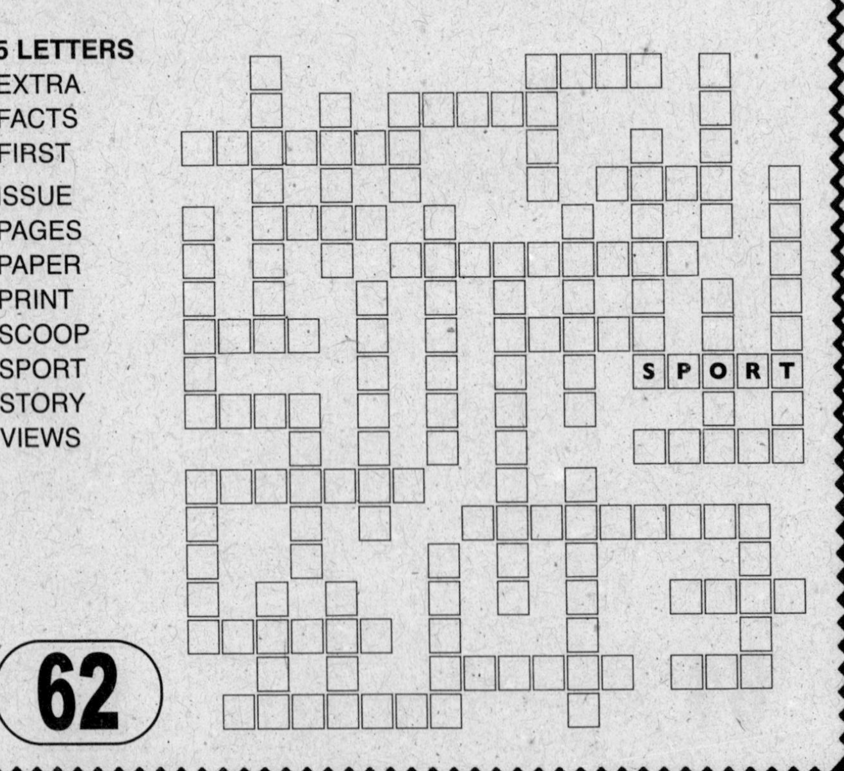

BE HAPPY

3 LETTERS
FUN
GAG
GAY
JOY
WIT

4 LETTERS
BEAM
GLAD
GLEE
GLOW
GRIN
JEST
JOKE
KISS

5 LETTERS
AMUSE
COMIC
JOLLY
LAUGH
LUCKY
MERRY
MIRTH
SMILE
SUNNY

6 LETTERS
CHEERY
ELATED
GIGGLE
HEAVEN

7 LETTERS
CHUCKLE
EMBRACE
EXCITED
FESTIVE
PLEASED

8 LETTERS
CHEERFUL
EUPHORIC
HUMOROUS
LAUGHTER

9 LETTERS
FORTUNATE

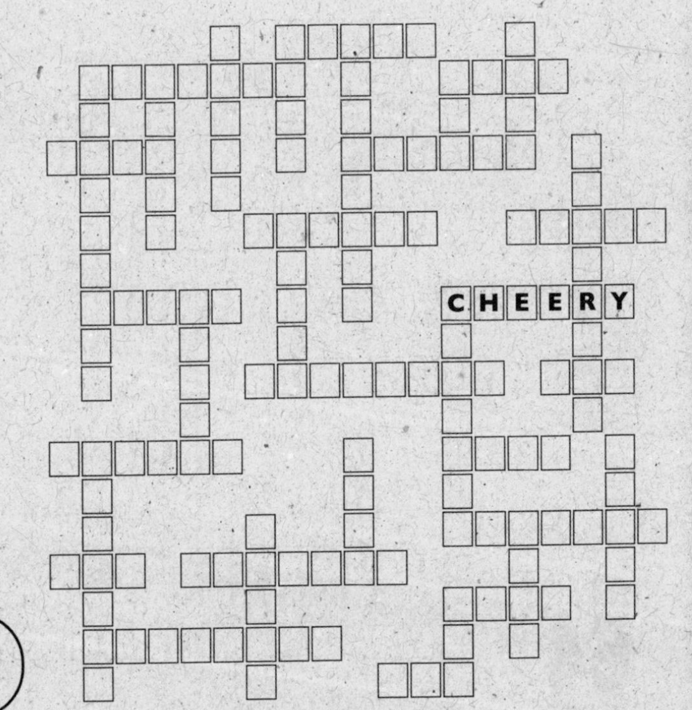

WHAT TO WEAR

3 LETTERS
BIB
BRA
CAP
FEZ
MAC
TIE
WIG

4 LETTERS
BELT
GOWN
KILT
MINI
MULE
SARI
SASH
SHOE
SUIT
TOGA

5 LETTERS
APRON
BOOTS
CLOAK
DRESS
PANTS
TRAIN

6 LETTERS
BIKINI
BLOUSE
BONNET
JACKET
JERSEY
KIMONO
SHORTS
TIGHTS
TRUNKS

7 LETTERS
GYMSLIP
LEOTARD
NIGHTIE
SWEATER

8 LETTERS
RAINCOAT
TROUSERS

9 LETTERS
HIGH HEELS
STOCKINGS

R A I N C O A T

MURDER MYSTERY

3 LETTERS
CRY
DIE

4 LETTERS
AXED
CLUB
DENY
DUEL
EDGY
EVER
FIRE
FREE
HERO
KILL
LIES
LIFE
LIMP
WIPE

5 LETTERS
ASHES
BLOOD
CHAOS
ENEMY
FIGHT
HAVOC
SPEED
TIRED
TWIST

6 LETTERS
ATTACK
DARKEN
DEFEND
FRIGHT
HATRED
MURDER
POISON
PYTHON
RIDDLE
SCHEME
SLEUTH
WEAKER

7 LETTERS
DILEMMA
EXPLAIN
HATCHET
LIBERTY
MYSTERY
SHATTER
SMASH UP
WHIMPER

H
E
R
O

ACCOUNTING

3 LETTERS
TAX
VAT

4 LETTERS
BANK
SALE
YEAR

5 LETTERS
CODES
DEBIT
ENTRY
RULES
TOTAL
VALUE

6 LETTERS
CHEQUE
CREDIT
MANUAL

7 LETTERS
BALANCE
JOURNAL
LEDGERS
NOMINAL
SURPLUS

8 LETTERS
ACCOUNTS
COMPUTER
PAYMENTS
PURCHASE
RECEIPTS

9 LETTERS
PETTY CASH
TAX RETURN

11 LETTERS
TRANSACTION

HOUSE SALE

3 LETTERS
BUY
FEE
GAS

4 LETTERS
AREA
COST
FLAT
GATE
HOME
MOVE
PACK
PLOT
SALE
SELL
SIGN

5 LETTERS
DRIVE
HOUSE
OFFER
PRICE
ROOMS

6 LETTERS
ADVERT
GARAGE
GARDEN
GROUND
LOUNGE
SURVEY
UNPACK

7 LETTERS
BEDROOM
DEPOSIT
FOR SALE
KITCHEN

8 LETTERS
COTTAGES
DETACHED
MORTGAGE
PROPERTY

9 LETTERS
VALUATION

11 LETTERS
ESTATE AGENT

O
F
F
E
R

LANGUAGE!

5 LETTERS
AZTEC
GREEK
HINDI
IRISH
LATIN
TAMIL
WELSH

6 LETTERS
ARABIC
DANISH
GERMAN
MAGYAR

7 LETTERS
BURMESE
CATALAN
ENGLISH
FLEMISH
ITALIAN
MALTESE
RUSSIAN
SPANISH

8 LETTERS
ARMENIAN
GUJARATI
JAPANESE
MANDARIN

9 LETTERS
ICELANDIC
NORWEGIAN
ROUMANIAN

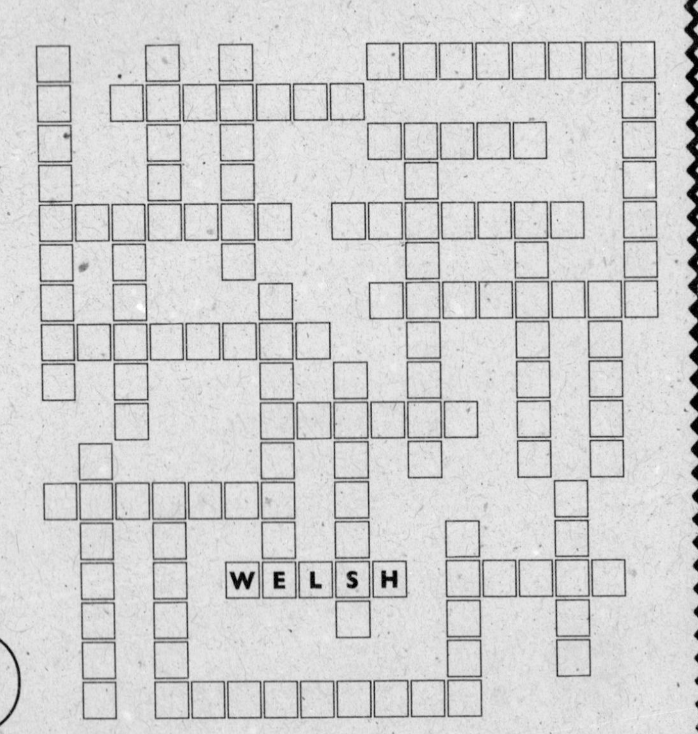

SCHOOL DAZE

3 LETTERS
ART
INK
NIB
PEN
SIR
SIT

4 LETTERS
DESK
DRAW
KIDS
READ
TERM

5 LETTERS
BOOKS
CHALK
LEARN
RULER
TEACH
WRITE

6 LETTERS
INFANT
LESSON
PENCIL
SCHOOL
SENIOR
SPORTS
TABLES

7 LETTERS
ENGLISH
HISTORY
INKWELL
SCIENCE
SUBJECT
TEACHER

8 LETTERS
ASSEMBLY
CHILDREN
HOMEWORK

9 LETTERS
CLASSROOM
EDUCATION

10 LETTERS
BLACKBOARD
HEADMASTER

S U B J E C T

LOOKING GOOD

3 LETTERS
BAG
TUB

4 LETTERS
CORD
DATE
HAIR
HOSE
IRON
LOOK
RUSH
SETS
SLIP
SOAP
SUIT
TRAY

5 LETTERS
BATHE
CURLS
DIALS
DRYER
HASTE
HOUSE
HURRY
RIGHT
RINGS
SHAVE
SHOES
START
TIMER
WATER

6 LETTERS
ADJUST
CHANGE
LIGHTS
MAKE-UP
SHOWER

7 LETTERS
FUSSING
HAIRPIN
MIRRORS
SHAMPOO

8 LETTERS
BUSINESS
DRESSING
GET READY
GROOMING

9 LETTERS
COSMETICS
EXTRA CARE

10 LETTERS
ATTACHMENT
COORDINATE
TOOTHBRUSH

D R Y E R

COURT ACTION

3 LETTERS
ACT
BAR
FEE
LAW

4 LETTERS
CASE
DOCK
FACT
JURY
OATH
RULE
SILK
VETO
WILL
WRIT

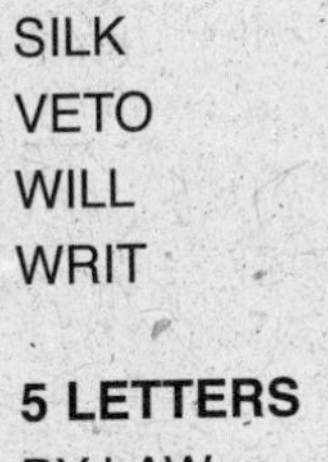

5 LETTERS
BY-LAW
CLAIM
COURT
COSTS
EDICT
LEGAL
PROOF
TRIAL
VOUCH

6 LETTERS
CAVEAT
GUILTY
LEGACY
PERMIT
SEA-LAW
SUB-LET
SURETY
TENURE
WAIVER

7 LETTERS
STATUTE

8 LETTERS
CHAMBERS
COVENANT
LENIENCE
PROPERTY
SUBPOENA
TEST-CASE

NUMERIC

3 LETTERS
MAN
ONE
TWO

4 LETTERS
BOOM
DEEP
LINE
OVER
TEST
TORT

5 LETTERS
AGENT
BASIS
CONIC
CURVE
ORBIT
SOLID
SPEED

6 LETTERS
CHANCE
MASTER
TRYING

7 LETTERS
BALANCE
CYCLOID
ETHICAL
PROLATE
SCIENCE
TANGENT

8 LETTERS
EINSTEIN
FINALITY
INFINITE
MULTIPLY
PARALLEL
RATIONAL
SYMMETRY

9 LETTERS
AGGREGATE
LOGARITHM
PARTITION

10 LETTERS
ARITHMETIC
INFALLIBLE

11 LETTERS
INDIVISIBLE
NUMERICALLY

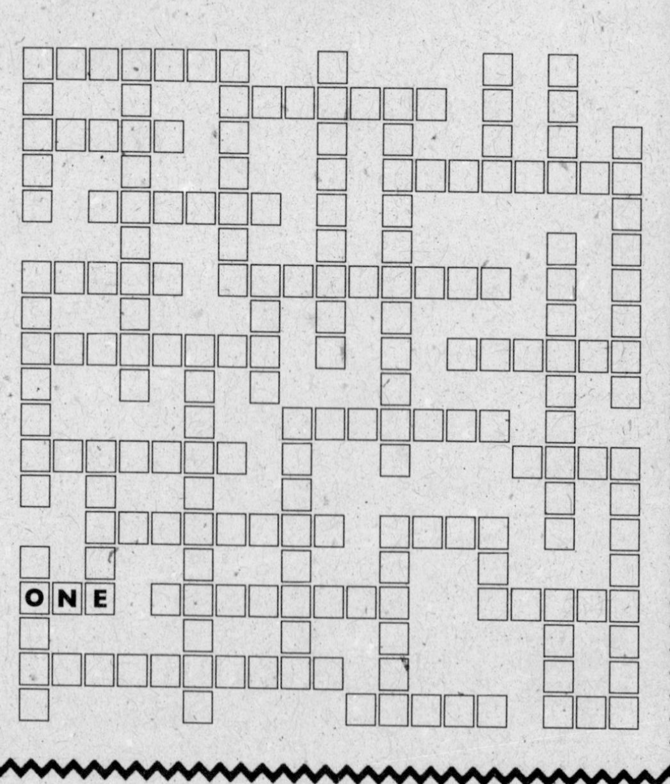

WHICH MAGAZINE?

Fit these words associated with weekly magazines into the grid.

3 LETTERS
ART
FIT
WIN

4 LETTERS
CASH
DIET
EDIT
LOOK
LOVE
NEWS
READ
SLIM
TIPS
TYPE

5 LETTERS
GIFTS
IDEAS
ISSUE
MONEY
PRINT
STYLE

6 LETTERS
ADVICE
EDITOR
FAMILY
HEALTH
INFORM
RECIPE
TRAVEL
WEEKLY
WINNER

7 LETTERS
ARTICLE
COOKERY
FASHION
FEATURE
LETTERS
READERS

8 LETTERS
CARTOONS
HOLIDAYS
MAGAZINE

11 LETTERS
COMPETITION

E D I T O R

PAINT BOX

3 LETTERS
BAY
RED
TAN

4 LETTERS
BLUE
FAWN
GREY
JADE
LIME
PINK
ROSE
RUBY
SAGE

5 LETTERS
AMBER
BEIGE
BROWN
CAMEL
CREAM
GREEN
LEMON
LILAC
OLIVE
WHITE

6 LETTERS
BRONZE
CHERRY
INDIGO
MAROON
ORANGE
SILVER
VIOLET
YELLOW

7 LETTERS
EMERALD
SCARLET
VERDANT

8 LETTERS
LAVENDER
PRIMROSE
SAPPHIRE

9 LETTERS
CARNATION
CHOCOLATE

10 LETTERS
TERRACOTTA

WIDE EYED

3 LETTERS
CRY
EYE
FAR
RED
SAW
USE
WET

4 LETTERS
BLUR
DEEP
LAZY

5 LETTERS
BLINK
DROOP
GLINT
HAZEL
PUPIL
RINGS
ROUND
SHAPE
SILLY
SNAKE
TENSE
TESTY

6 LETTERS
DREAMY
FIERCE
MYOPIC
NARROW
RECESS
SEEING
SLEEPY
WATERS
WEEPER

7 LETTERS
ADORING
BEDROOM
GLARING
GLITTER
PROBING
STARING

8 LETTERS
BABY-BLUE
CRINGING
FEARLESS
GRIEVING
ORIENTAL
SERAPHIC
WIDE-EYED

9 LETTERS
BEAUTIFUL
EAGLE-EYED
EMOTIONAL

10 LETTERS
ASTIGMATIC
EVER-ROVING
EXPRESSIVE
STARRY-EYED

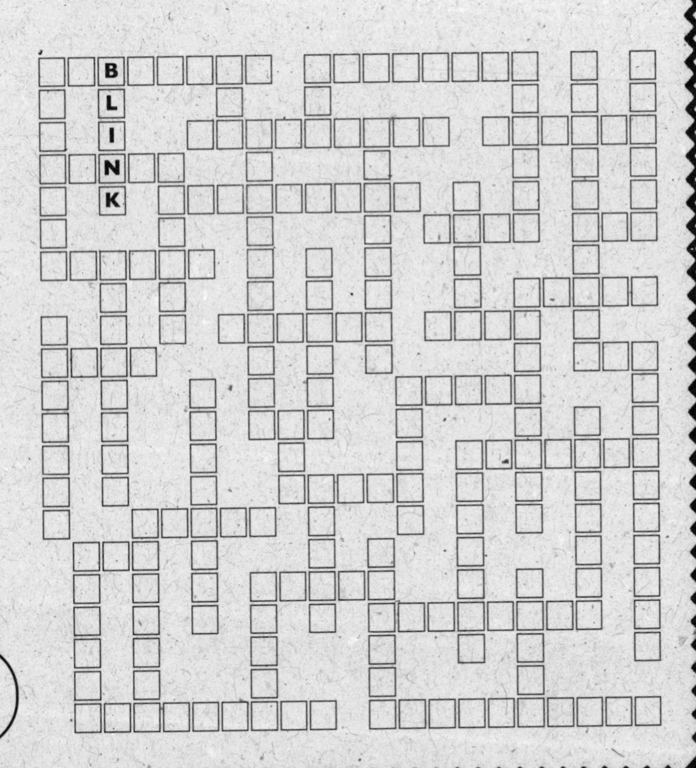

HOLIDAY TIME

3 LETTERS
SEA
SUN

4 LETTERS
HEAT
MEAL
POOL

5 LETTERS
BREAK
COAST
CORFU
DISCO
DRIVE
RELAX
RIVER
SANDY
VILLA
VISIT

6 LETTERS
ISLAND
LUXURY
RESORT
SUNHAT
TRAVEL
TURKEY

7 LETTERS
COUNTRY
HOLIDAY
ONE WEEK
TOURIST

8 LETTERS
PASSPORT
PORTUGAL
SUNBATHE

9 LETTERS
AUSTRALIA
FORTNIGHT

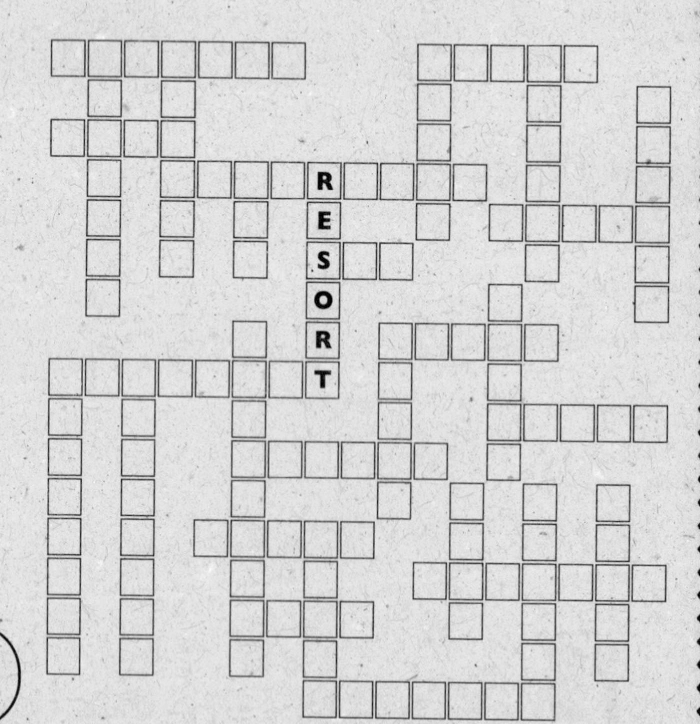

BIRD WATCH

3 LETTERS
DAW
MOA
OWL
ROC

4 LETTERS
CHAT
COOT
HAWK
RHEA
SKUA
TERN

5 LETTERS
DIVER
GOOSE
GREBE
HERON
OUSEL

6 LETTERS
AVOCET
BANTAM
CHOUGH
GROUSE
LINNET
MAGPIE
OSPREY
PARROT
PETREL
PIGEON

7 LETTERS
BARN OWL
BLUE TIT
BUSTARD
BUZZARD
COAL TIT
CREEPER
DUNNOCK
JACKDAW
SPARROW

P A R R O T

IN UNISON

3 LETTERS
AID
ARM
MIX
OWN
TEA
TWO
WED
WOO

4 LETTERS
CHAT
COSY
DEAR
HOLD
KNOT
LOVE
RING
SNUG
SONG
TEAM

5 LETTERS
ARROW
BLOOD
CLOSE
CROWD
GUEST
PEACE
SCOLD
SHARE
SPORT
SWEET
TWINS
UNITY

6 LETTERS
DOTING
EROTIC
FIANCE
LIMPET
SECRET
SMOOCH
UNISON
WARMTH

7 LETTERS
COMBINE
COMFORT
KINSHIP
KISSING
KNOWING
PROTECT
SINCERE

K
N
O
T

PAY PLASTIC

Fit the credit card words into the grid.

3 LETTERS
BUY
PAY

4 LETTERS
BANK
CARD
CASH
DATA
DATE
FORM
OPEN
SCAN
SHOP
SIGN

5 LETTERS
CARRY
DEBIT
HANDY
LIMIT
MONEY
REPAY
SPEND
VALID

6 LETTERS
CHARGE
CREDIT
NUMBER
TRAVEL
USEFUL

7 LETTERS
ACCOUNT
ADDRESS
BENEFIT
COUNTER
HOLIDAY

8 LETTERS
FLEXIBLE
INTEREST
PURCHASE

9 LETTERS
CUSTOMERS
DISPENSER

B A N K

IN KENT

Take a visit to Kent, the garden of England, and fit the words into the grid.

3 LETTERS
BAY
WYE

4 LETTERS
DEAL
FARM
HOPS
KENT
LYDD
OAST
PORT

5 LETTERS
CHALK
DOCKS
DOVER
HERNE
HILLS
HOUSE
HYTHE
KNOLE
LEEDS
MARSH
RIVER
SHEEP
TOWNS
WEALD
WOODS

6 LETTERS
CASTLE
CINQUE
CLIFFS
GARDEN
MEDWAY
ROMNEY
TUNNEL

7 LETTERS
ASHFORD
CHANNEL
CHATHAM
MARGATE

8 LETTERS
SANDWICH

10 LETTERS
CANTERBURY

M A R G A T E

INSTRUMENTAL

3 LETTERS
BAR
BOW
KEY

4 LETTERS
BASE
BASS
CLEF
DRUM
FLAT
HORN
NOTE
PLAY
REST
SING
SONG
TONE
TUNE

5 LETTERS
FLUTE
HARPS
MAJOR
MINIM
MUSIC
OBOES
ORGAN
PIANO
PITCH
SHARP
STAVE

6 LETTERS
CHORDS
GUITAR
MELODY
OCTAVE
RHYTHM
SCALES
VIOLIN

7 LETTERS
NATURAL
REFRAIN

8 LETTERS
CROTCHET
KEYBOARD
TROMBONE

9 LETTERS
SAXOPHONE

10 LETTERS
INSTRUMENT

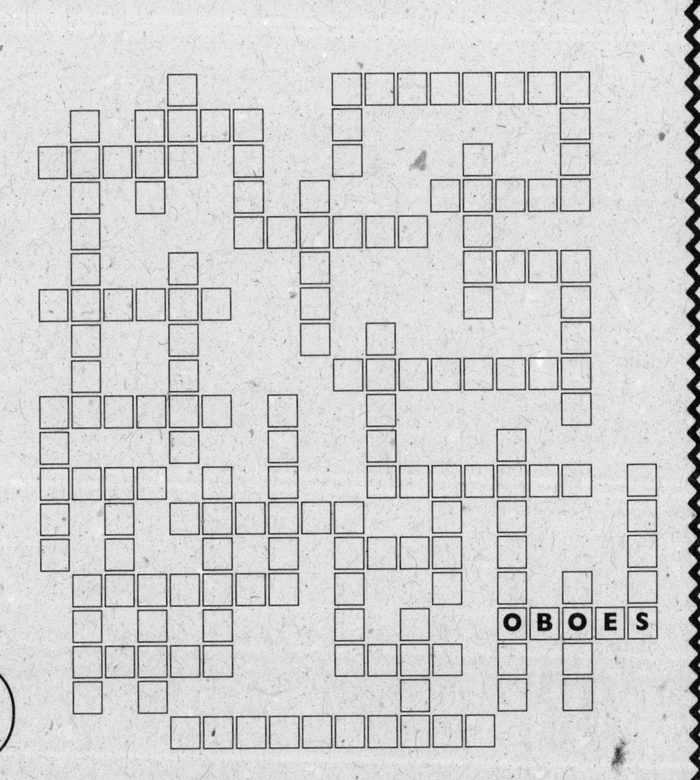

SNOOKERED

3 LETTERS
CUE
POT
TIP

4 LETTERS
BLUE
DRAG
FOUL
KISS
MISS
PINK
REDS
REST
SIDE
SPIN
SPOT

5 LETTERS
BALLS
BLACK
BREAK
BROWN
CLEAN
FRAME
PLANT
SCORE
TABLE
WHITE

6 LETTERS
CANNON
POCKET
SPIDER
YELLOW

7 LETTERS
COLOURS
CUSHION
GLANCED
MAXIMUM
REFEREE
SNOOKER

8 LETTERS
TRIANGLE

9 LETTERS
BAULK LINE

SIZEABLE

3 LETTERS
DAB
DOT
FAT
WEE

4 LETTERS
GONE
LEAN
MINI
MITE
SLIM
TALL
TINY
TRIM
WEAK

5 LETTERS
DWARF
ELFIN
GREAT
OBESE
PLUMP
TEENY
THICK
TITAN

6 LETTERS
DAINTY
FLESHY
FRINGE
LITTLE
MERGER
MIGHTY
PEEWEE
ROBUST
ROTUND

7 LETTERS
ADIPOSE
ENDLESS
FRAGILE
IMMENSE
STUNTED
TRIVIAL

8 LETTERS
COLOSSUS
ENGORGED
FRACTION
GIGANTIC
PINPOINT
TOWERING
UNWIELDY

9 LETTERS
CYCLOPEAN
EXPANSIVE
EXTENSIVE
MICROCOSM
MINIATURE
STRAPPING
UNLIMITED

10 LETTERS
STUPENDOUS
VOLUMINOUS

FIX IT!

3 LETTERS
FIX
LAY
SET

4 LETTERS
BIND
CLIP
CURE
HEAL
MEND
MOOR

5 LETTERS
ADAPT
AFFIX
AMEND
BRACE
COVER
PATCH
REFIT
RIVET
STILL

6 LETTERS
ADJUST
ANCHOR
ATTACH
DECIDE
DOCTOR
FASTEN
REMEDY
REPAIR
SECURE
STEADY

7 LETTERS
CONNECT
CORRECT
OVERLAY
RESOLVE
RESTORE
SERVICE

8 LETTERS
OVERHAUL

9 LETTERS
ESTABLISH

STEADY

FACE FACTS

3 LETTERS
DRY

4 LETTERS
BALM
CARE
KOHL
MASK
MATT
SKIN
SOAP
SOFT
TINT

5 LETTERS
CREAM
SHADE
SHEER
TONER

6 LETTERS
DEFINE
FACIAL
GENTLE
LOTION
MAKE-UP
NORMAL
PASTEL
POWDER

7 LETTERS
BRONZER
MASCARA
NATURAL

8 LETTERS
EYELINER
LIPLINER
LIPSTICK
SKINCARE

10 LETTERS
ASTRINGENT
REVITALISE
WATERPROOF

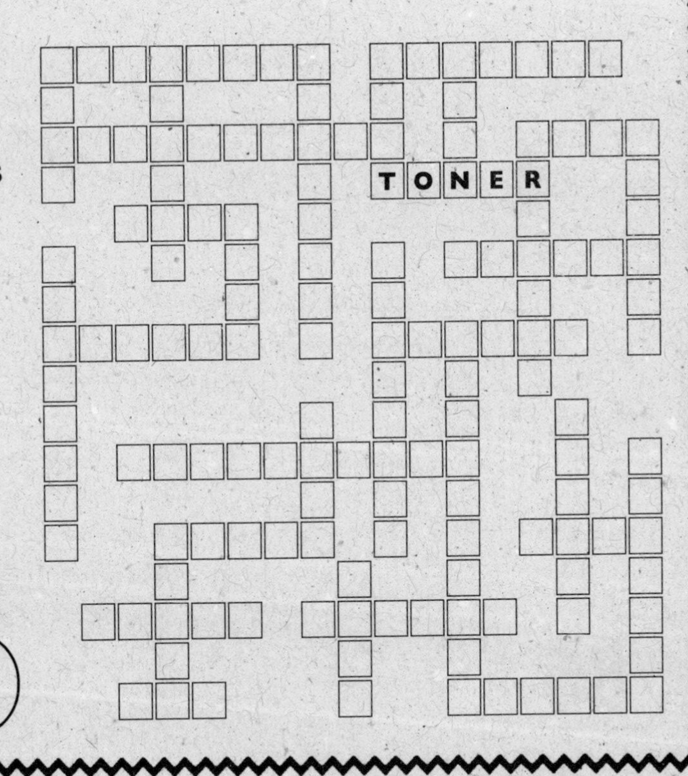

UP ABOVE

3 LETTERS
ADS
CAP
DIP
FOG
ICE
SUN
TEE

4 LETTERS
BOOM
BUGS
CUSP
EVER
FAIR
HALO
JETS
MOON
PEAK
SILO
STAR
VANE

5 LETTERS
BIRDS
CLOUD
COMET
CREST
FLARE
FROST
KITES
NESTS
PLANE
SMOKE
SPIRE
TOWER
TREES
WIRES

6 LETTERS
BEACON
BELFRY
CABLES
CRANES
LEAVES

7 LETTERS
ANTENNA
BALLOON
INSECTS
PLANETS
ROCKETS
STEEPLE

8 LETTERS
FLAGPOLE
WINDSOCK

9 LETTERS
PARACHUTE
SPACESHIP

SOUNDS RIGHT

3 LETTERS
AIR
BAA
CAW
COO
CRY
EAR
HUE
LOW
OLE!
YAK

4 LETTERS
AVER
BARK
BLAB
BLOW
BRAG
GUSH
HISS
HOWL
LA LA
MEOW
PURR
RAGE
RAIL
RAKE
RANT
ROAR
SOLO
SONG
STUN
TAPS

5 LETTERS
CRACK
CROAK
FORCE
GROWL
SWEAR
TWANG
VOICE
WEEPY

6 LETTERS
ACCENT
BELLOW
CAVILS
ECHOES
PRATES
SCREAM
SQUEAL
TINKLE

7 LETTERS
CATCALL
CHATTER
GURGLES
NARRATE
PRATTLE
SCREECH
SQUAWKS
STUTTER
THUNDER
TWITTER
WHINERS
WHISPER
WHISTLE

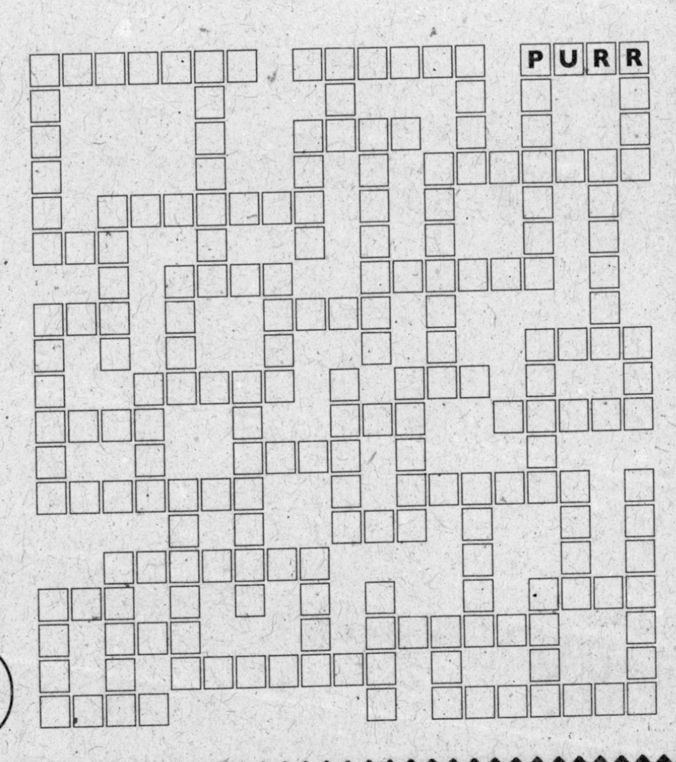

FIFTEEN & FOUR

4 LETTERS
ATOM
AXIL
CORN
CUTE
DEAR
DRAM
EARN
HELM
HERE
INCH
IRIS
ISLE
LIRA
LOST
MILD
NEXT
OMEN
PAST
RATE
SAME
SING
TALK
TELL
TOOT
TUNE
YELP

15 LETTERS
DREDGING-MACHINE
ELECTRO-MAGNETIC
INAPPROPRIATELY
INCOMPREHENSIVE
INSTRUMENTALIST

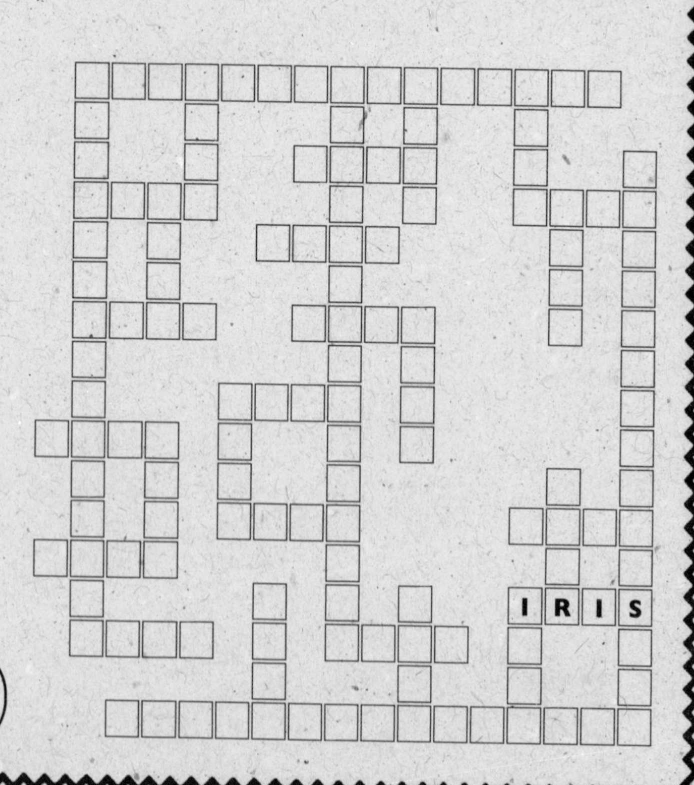

KEEP SLIM

3 LETTERS
ASK
BAR
CUT
JOG
PEP
SPA

4 LETTERS
ACHE
AVID
CASH
DIET
GOLF
LOSE
MATS
PACE
PADS
SAFE
SKIP
SKIS
SWIM
UNIT
WALK
YOGA

5 LETTERS
BOOKS
CLUBS
FASTS
FRUIT
GROUP
JUICE
NO FAT
PILLS
PLANS
SALAD
SALON
SAUNA
STEAM
STOOP
TWIST

6 LETTERS
ADDS UP
NO SALT
REDUCE
STAGES
WEIGHT

7 LETTERS
BICYCLE
EAT LESS
MASSAGE
PROTEIN
PULLEYS
PUSH-UPS
STRETCH
THERAPY
WORK OUT

8 LETTERS
AEROBICS
CALORIES
LEOTARDS
NO SWEETS
ROUGHAGE
SKIM MILK

9 LETTERS
EXERCISES
NO ALCOHOL

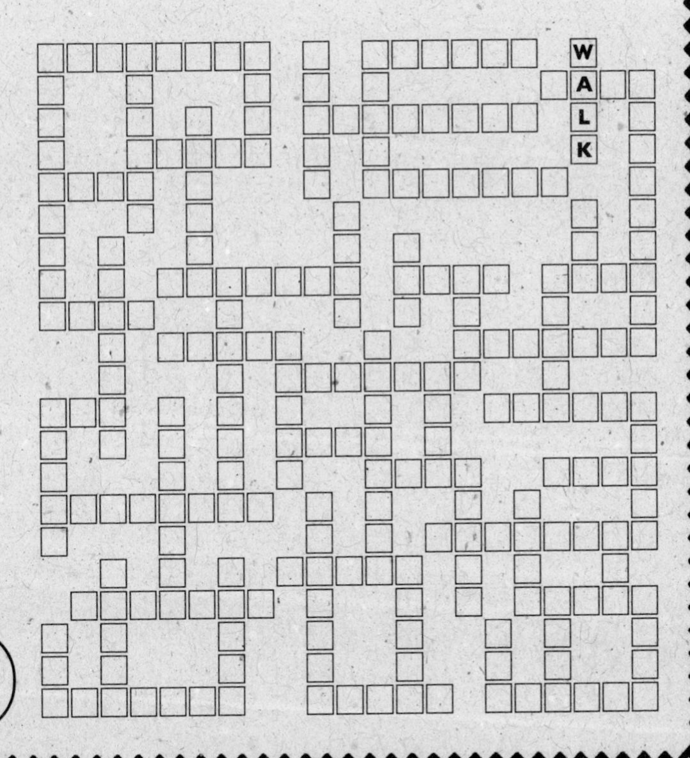

THAT'S A BOY

3 LETTERS
DON
JIM
NED
RON

4 LETTERS
ALAN
BILL
FRED
JACK
JOSH
NOEL
PAUL

5 LETTERS
BENNY
BRIAN
BRUCE
COLIN
DAVID
ERNIE
FRANK
HENRY
JASON
PERCY
ROGER
TOMMY

6 LETTERS
DANIEL
DONALD
GERALD
HOWARD
MARTIN
OLIVER
SAMUEL

7 LETTERS
KENNETH
LEONARD
PATRICK

8 LETTERS
CLARENCE
HARRISON
LAWRENCE

9 LETTERS
ARCHIBALD

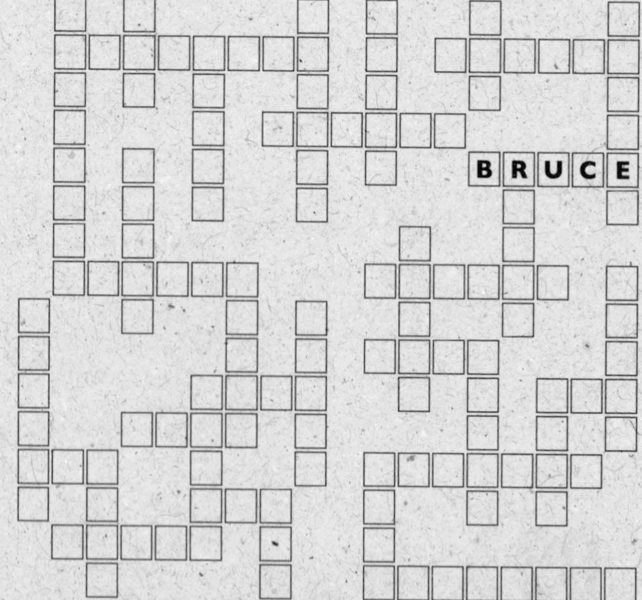

BRANCH LINE

3 LETTERS
ASH
ELM
FIG
SAP
YEW

4 LETTERS
ALOE
BARK
KNOT
PINE
ROOT
TWIG

5 LETTERS
ACORN
ALDER
APPLE
ASPEN
BIRCH
CEDAR
ELDER
GLADE
LILAC
MAPLE
OLIVE
ROWAN

6 LETTERS
BANYAN
CHERRY
FOREST
KAURIS
LEAVES
POPLAR
SPRUCE
WILLOW

7 LETTERS
COLOURS
CONIFER

8 LETTERS
BRANCHES
CHESTNUT
SAPLINGS
SYCAMORE

9 LETTERS
DECIDUOUS
EVERGREEN

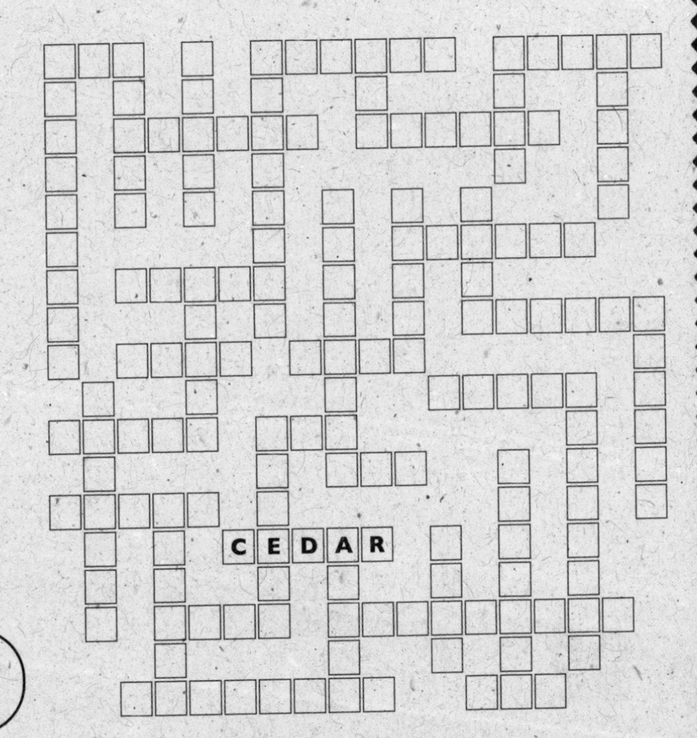

SEASIDERS

3 LETTERS
COX
SEA
SUB
TAR

4 LETTERS
BEAM
BUOY
CORK
CREW
FOAM
HEAD
HELM
IDLE
LOCK
MAST
NAVY
OPEN
POOP
PORT
PROW
REEF
SAIL
SHIP
SPIN
STAY
TACK
VEER

5 LETTERS
AWASH
BELOW
BERTH
CABIN
COAST
FERRY
HATCH
LINER
SLOOP

6 LETTERS
AFLOAT
CANVAS
HAWSER
LAUNCH

7 LETTERS
CAPSIZE
RIPTIDE
SEASICK
SEAWARD
STEWARD
TOPSAIL

STEAM AGE

3 LETTERS
ERA
OIL
RUN

4 LETTERS
COAL
FIRE
FUEL
HEAT
HISS
LINE
RAIL
RIDE
SEAT
SLOW
TANK

5 LETTERS
DOORS
GAUGE
SMELL
SMOKE
STEAM
TRAIN

6 LETTERS
ARRIVE
DEPART
DRIVER
ENGINE
FUNNEL
SIGNAL
STOKER
TENDER

7 LETTERS
STATION
WHISTLE

8 LETTERS
GRADIENT
PLATFORM
PRESERVE

9 LETTERS
CARRIAGES
NOSTALGIA

10 LETTERS
PASSENGERS

IN THE KITCHEN

3 LETTERS
CUP
HOB
GAS

4 LETTERS
DISH
OVEN
PANS
RAIL
SINK
TAPS

5 LETTERS
CLOCK
GRILL
RANGE
SHELF
TOWEL
UNITS

6 LETTERS
CHAIRS
COOKER
DRAWER
FRIDGE
PLATES
SCALES
TABLES
TEAPOT
WINDOW

7 LETTERS
CABINET
CUTLERY
DRAINER
KETTLES
KITCHEN

8 LETTERS
CROCKERY
ELECTRIC
HOT WATER
SURFACES

10 LETTERS
DISHWASHER
SPLASHBACK

IRON OUT

3 LETTERS
DRY
HOT

4 LETTERS
BURN
COOL
CORD
FILL
PLUG
SEAR
SILK
TANK
WARM
WOOL

5 LETTERS
BOARD
PRESS
RAYON
SHIRT
SPRAY
STEAM
WATER

6 LETTERS
ADJUST
BUTTON
FABRIC
SCORCH
SMOOTH
SWITCH

7 LETTERS
CLOTHES
COTTONS
CREASES

8 LETTERS
CORDLESS
ELECTRIC
IRONING
TROUSERS

9 LETTERS
SOLE PLATE

11 LETTERS
TEMPERATURE

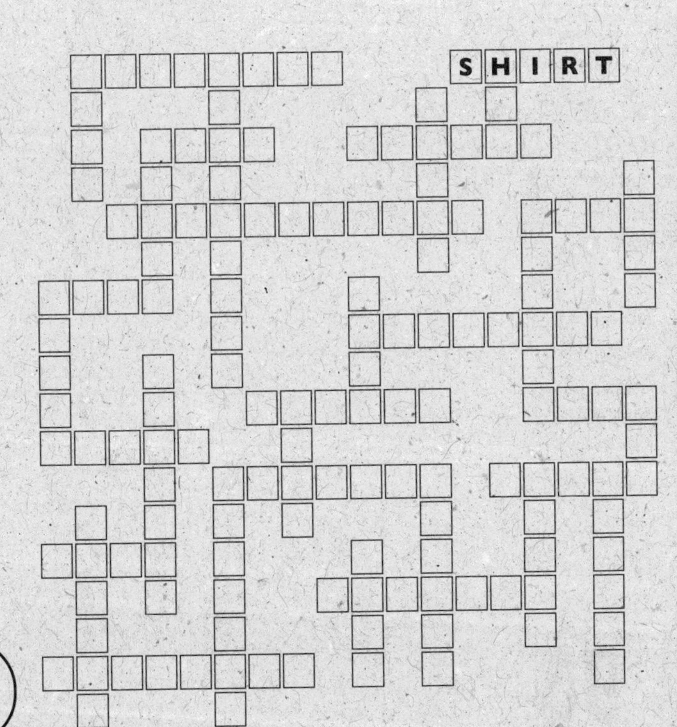

DAILY DISH

3 LETTERS
EAT
HOT
JUG

4 LETTERS
BOWL
BRAN
DISH
IRON
MALT
MILK
NUTS
OATS
POUR
RICE

5 LETTERS
DAILY
FIBRE
FRUIT
MAIZE
SPOON
START
SUGAR
TASTY
WHEAT

6 LETTERS
CEREAL
ENERGY
MUESLI
NIACIN
PACKET

7 LETTERS
POPCORN
RAISINS
SERVING

8 LETTERS
MINERALS
PORRIDGE
VITAMINS

9 LETTERS
BREAKFAST
NUTRITION

10 LETTERS
CORNFLAKES

B R A N

IN A SPIN

3 LETTERS
DRY

4 LETTERS
FAST
FOAM
LINE
LOAD
PEGS
SOAK
SOIL
SPIN
SUDS
VEST
WASH
WOOL

5 LETTERS
CLEAN
CYCLE
NYLON
RINSE
SHEET
SHIRT
SOCKS
STAIN
WATER

6 LETTERS
COTTON
DRYING
FABRIC
LATHER
LINENS
LIQUID
POWDER
ROTATE
WASHER
WHITES

7 LETTERS
MACHINE
PREWASH

8 LETTERS
TROUSERS

9 LETTERS
COLOUREDS

11 LETTERS
TEMPERATURE

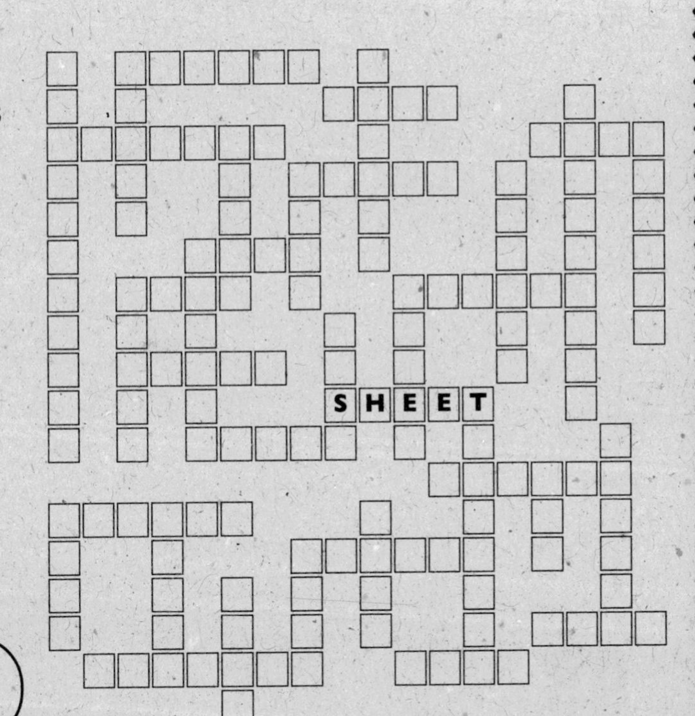

BUSINESS MATTERS

3 LETTERS
ACT
ADD
BID
DUE
FEE
RIG
SUM
TAX

4 LETTERS
DEAL
EARN
FAIR
HIRE
LEND
RENT
SALE
VISA

5 LETTERS
AUDIT
CHORE
CLERK
MISER
OWING
REMIT
TOKEN
TRADE

6 LETTERS
CARTEL
CLIENT
ESTATE
GROWTH
MERGER
OFFICE
PUBLIC
RETAIL
SETTLE
UNPAID

7 LETTERS
ACCOUNT
DEPOSIT
LOTTERY
PAYABLE

A C T

BORING STUFF

3 LETTERS
BIT
KEY
SET

4 LETTERS
BORE
CASE
HOLE
JAWS
LOCK
SIZE
STOP
VOLT
WALL
WOOD

5 LETTERS
CABLE
CHUCK
DEPTH
DRIVE
GEARS
METAL
PLUGS
SCREW
SPEED

6 LETTERS
ADJUST
BORING
CHARGE
DRILLS
HAMMER
HANDLE
SINGLE
SWITCH
TORQUE

7 LETTERS
BATTERY
FORWARD
MASONRY
REVERSE

8 LETTERS
CORDLESS
DRILLING
ELECTRIC
VARIABLE

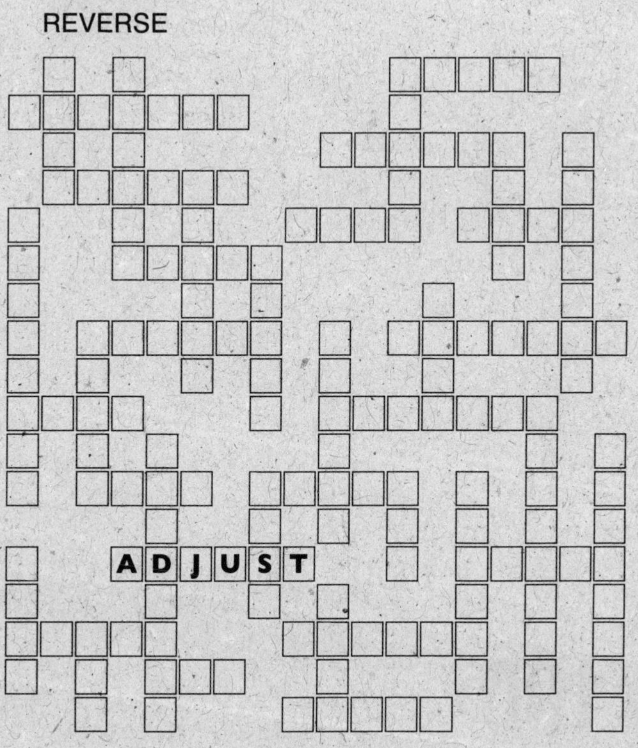

COOKER CATCH

3 LETTERS
FRY
HOT
PAN
TIN

4 LETTERS
BAKE
BURN
DISH
FOOD
FOUR
GRID
HEAT
HIGH
KNOB
OVEN
PANS
PUSH
TURN

5 LETTERS
CLEAN
FLAME
FRAME
GRILL
LEVEL
LIGHT
METAL
PANEL
PILOT
PRESS
RINGS
SHELF
STOVE
TRAYS

6 LETTERS
BUTTON
CANOPY
COOKER
SWITCH

7 LETTERS
BATTERY
GRIDDLE
HEATING
IGNITION
KITCHEN

C L E A N

FAST FORWARD

Fit the video words into the grid.

3 LETTERS
TAB

4 LETTERS
BACK
LOAD
MODE
PLAY
SEEK
STOP
TAPE
TIME
TUNE
VIEW

5 LETTERS
CABLE
CLEAR
EJECT
ERASE
FRAME
START
TIMER
VIDEO
WATCH

6 LETTERS
ADJUST
DIRECT
INSERT
RECORD
REWIND

7 LETTERS
BUTTONS
COUNTER
DISPLAY
FORWARD
HANDSET
PICTURE
SETTING

8 LETTERS
CASSETTE
TRANSFER

9 LETTERS
PROGRAMME

11 LETTERS
FAST FORWARD

P I C T U R E

HAPPY HOLIDAYS

3 LETTERS
CAR
HOT
SEA

4 LETTERS
CITY
LAZY
MEET
PACK
SWIM

5 LETTERS
BEACH
COACH
HOTEL
ITALY
MALTA
PLANE
SHOPS
YACHT

6 LETTERS
CRUISE
CYPRUS
FAMILY
GREECE
THE MED
TICKET
UNPACK

7 LETTERS
AIRPORT
FLORIDA
FRIENDS
JOURNEY
MADIERA
MOROCCO

8 LETTERS
HONG KONG

9 LETTERS
THEMEPARK

T H E M E P A R K

LET'S DANCE

3 LETTERS
BOP
JIG

4 LETTERS
BALL
JIVE
JOTA
REEL

5 LETTERS
BEBOP
CAPER
FLING
RUMBA
SAMBA
TANGO
TWIST

6 LETTERS
BOLERO
CHA-CHA
MINUET
MORRIS
PAVANE
SHIMMY
VALETA

7 LETTERS
LA VOLTA
MADISON
ONE-STEP
TWO-STEP

8 LETTERS
FANDANGO
HORNPIPE
RIGADOON
SARABAND

9 LETTERS
BOSSA NOVA
PAUL JONES
PIRQUETTE

10 LETTERS
CHARLESTON

SHAPELY

3 LETTERS
ARC
BOX

4 LETTERS
BASE
CONE
CUBE
LINE
OVAL
STAR

5 LETTERS
ANGLE
EDGES
HELIX
OVOID
POINT

6 LETTERS
ARROWS
CENTRE
CIRCLE
CURVED
LINEAR
OBLONG
SPHERE
SPIRAL

7 LETTERS
CROSSES
DIAMOND
ELLIPSE
HEXAGON
OCTAGON
POLYGON

8 LETTERS
TRIANGLE

9 LETTERS
PYRAMIDAL
RECTANGLE

T R I A N G L E

COURT ORDER

3 LETTERS
AGE
RUE

4 LETTERS
ACTS
EASE
LAWS
NULL
TAPE
TEST

5 LETTERS
BIBLE
CLERK
COURT
FACTS
JUDGE
SENSE
TRIAL
WILLS

6 LETTERS
ACTION
DEBATE
ERRORS
ISSUES
LATEST
LAWYER
RATIFY
RECESS
RELENT
TRUSTS

7 LETTERS
ADDRESS
EFFECTS
EXCUSES
LETTERS
OFFICER
PERJURY

8 LETTERS
ATTITUDE
LEGALITY
MEDIATOR
STANDARD
SUSPENSE

9 LETTERS
ABSENTEES
ELOQUENCE
LIBRARIAN
WITNESSES

10 LETTERS
OUT OF ORDER
SPECTATORS

T R I A L

IN THE STARS

Can you fit the fortune-telling words into the grid?

3 LETTERS
LEO
TEA

4 LETTERS
BALL
BORN
CASH
DATE
LUCK
MARS
PALM
READ
STAR
WORK

5 LETTERS
ARIES
CHART
HANDS
LIBRA
MONEY
SIGNS
TAROT
VENUS
VIRGO

6 LETTERS
CANCER
GEMINI
HEALTH
LEAVES
PISCES
PLANET
REVEAL
TAURUS
WEALTH

7 LETTERS
CRYSTAL
FORTUNE
SCORPIO

8 LETTERS
AQUARIUS
FORECAST

9 LETTERS
CAPRICORN

11 LETTERS
SAGITTARIUS

TAURUS

DEBATABLE

Fit these parliamentary words into the grid.

3 LETTERS
BEN
BIG
FOR
MPS

4 LETTERS
AYES
BACK
HALL
MACE
NOES
SEAT
TORY
WHIP

5 LETTERS
BENCH
CHAIR
CLOCK
ELECT
FRONT
LOBBY
LORDS
PARTY
REPLY
SPEAK
TOWER

6 LETTERS
DEBATE
HOUSES
LABOUR
MEMBER
PUBLIC

7 LETTERS
AGAINST
CHAMBER
COMMONS
LIBERAL
SPEAKER

8 LETTERS
WOOLSACK

10 LETTERS
PARLIAMENT

11 LETTERS
WESTMINSTER

E L E C T

WHERE ON EARTH

3 LETTERS
AGE
AIR
BAR
BAY
ICE
ORE
RIM
SEA
TIN

4 LETTERS
ALPS
AXIS
LOAM
MOSS
RISE
SAND

5 LETTERS
ARADA
CORAL
EARTH
HAZES
MARSH
NORTH
OASIS
OCEAN
POLES

6 LETTERS
GEYSER
ISLAND
MOLTEN
PLAINS

7 LETTERS
ALLUVIA
COUNTRY
EROSION
GEOLOGY
GLACIER
HORIZON
PASTURE
SCENERY
STRIDES

8 LETTERS
ALTITUDE
AND TERRA
ICEBERGS
RARE CLAY

9 LETTERS
GEOGRAPHY
GRASSLAND
GREAT SEAS
LIMESTONE

POP POURRI

Pop the words into the grid.

3 LETTERS
HIT
MUD
POP

4 LETTERS
BASS
BEAT
DANA
JOHN
OBOE
PAUL
ROCK
TUBA
WHAM

5 LETTERS
ALBUM
CHART
ELVIS
GROUP
LYRIC
MUSIC
NOISE
RINGO
SLADE
SONGS
STING
TRACK
TUNES
WINGS

6 LETTERS
BONEY M
GEORGE
RECORD
SINGLE
TOP TEN

7 LETTERS
ADAM ANT
BEATLES
MADNESS
MADONNA
SHADOWS

8 LETTERS
KATE BUSH
TOM JONES

9 LETTERS
ADAM FAITH
ELTON JOHN

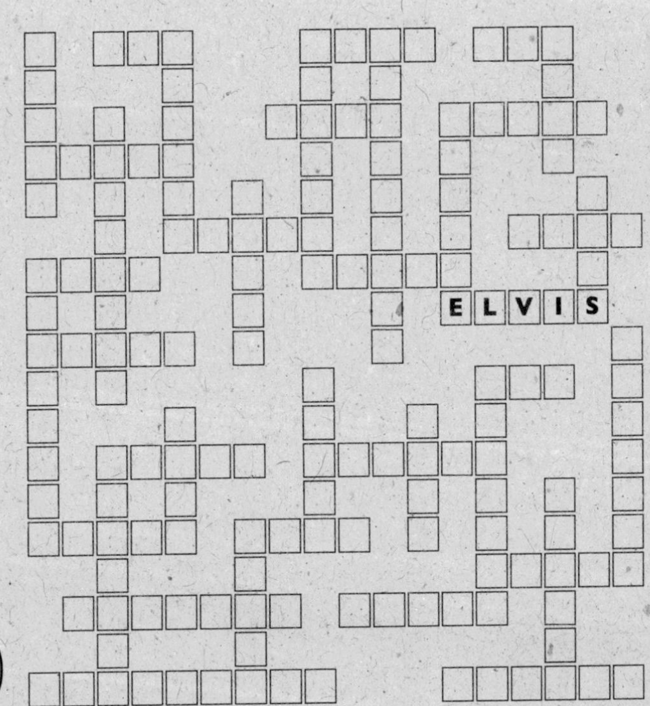

TAKE TIME

2 LETTERS
AM
PM

3 LETTERS
DAY
MAY

4 LETTERS
DAWN
DUSK
JULY
WEEK
YEAR

5 LETTERS
APRIL
MARCH

6 LETTERS
AUGUST
FRIDAY
MONDAY
SUNDAY

7 LETTERS
EVENING
JANUARY
MORNING
OCTOBER
TUESDAY

8 LETTERS
DECEMBER
FEBRUARY
NOVEMBER
SATURDAY

9 LETTERS
AFTERNOON
SEPTEMBER
WEDNESDAY

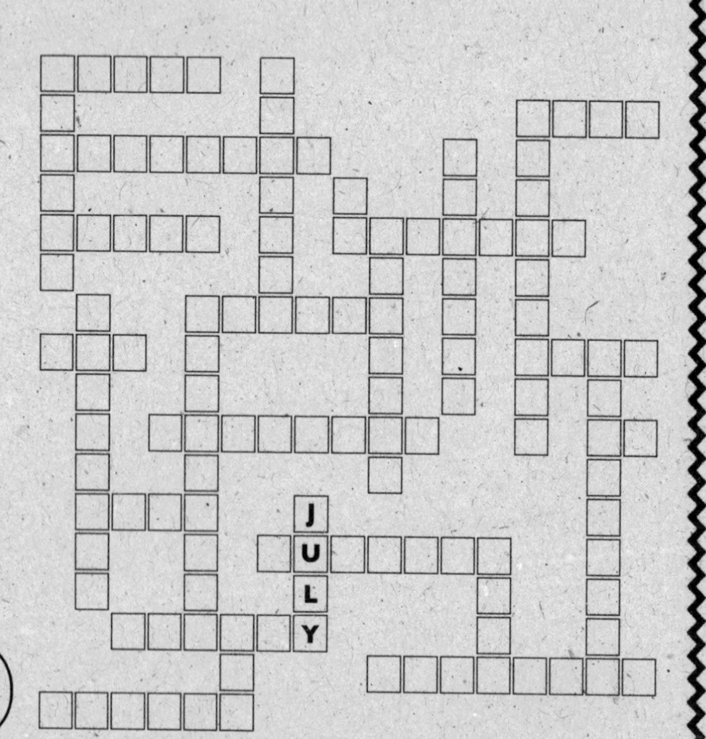

FOOD FAD

3 LETTERS
ALE
BAR
BUN
CAN
CUP
HAM
OIL
PIE
TEA
TUB

4 LETTERS
BEEF
BRAN
CHOP
DISH
FLAN
LOAF
PORK
SALT
SOUP
STEW
SUET
TART
TOSS
WHEY

5 LETTERS
CURRY
DOUGH
FLOUR
GRAVY
ICING
KEBAB
LIVER
STEAK

6 LETTERS
BUTTER
CAVIAR
MUFFIN
SUNDAE

7 LETTERS
BANQUET
BISCUIT
CRUMPET
KETCHUP
PANCAKE
RATAFIA

T
A
R
T

MIXED BAG

3 LETTERS
ACE
FAN
NUN
RAT
VET
WIT

4 LETTERS
BOSS
CHAR
COOK
FOOL
HOBO
LOUT
OGRE
SERF
STAR
TWIT

5 LETTERS
COMIC
NAVVY
RIVAL
STOIC

6 LETTERS
ARTIST
BEAUTY
CASUAL
COWARD
GIGOLO
OUTLAW
PUNDIT
STOOGE
SUITOR
TYCOON

7 LETTERS
BOUNCER
CITIZEN
EGGHEAD
HERETIC
INFIDEL
KNOW-ALL
NUTCASE
RECLUSE
STUDENT
UPSTART
WITNESS

GOING PLACES

3 LETTERS
BUS
CAR
ROW

4 LETTERS
BOAT
DOCK
LINE
LOCK
PORT
RANK
RIDE
SAIL
SHIP
SPIN
TAXI
TOUR
TREK
TUBE

5 LETTERS
A-ROAD
CANAL
CYCLE
DEPOT
PLANE
TRAIN

6 LETTERS
CRUISE
GARAGE
SUBWAY
VOYAGE

7 LETTERS
AIRPORT
RAILWAY
STATION

11 LETTERS
BRIDLE PATHS
NARROW BOATS
SPACE TRAVEL
UNDERGROUND

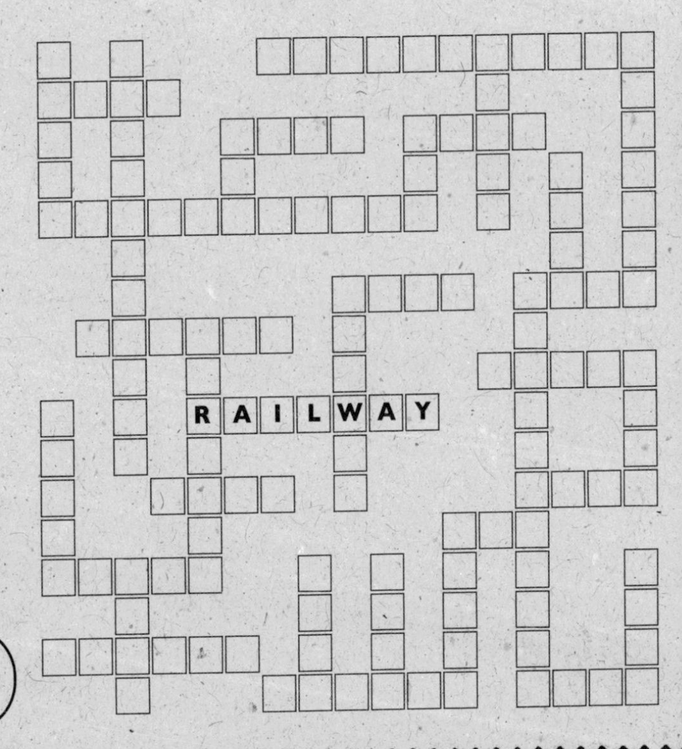

WASHED UP

Clean up this puzzle by fitting the words into the grid.

3 LETTERS
CUP
DRY
HOT
RUB

4 LETTERS
BOWL
FILL
FOAM
FOOD
FORK
MILD
PANS
PLUG
POTS
RACK
TAPS
WASH
WIPE

5 LETTERS
CLEAN
GLEAM
HANDS
KNIFE
PLATE
RINSE
SHINE
SPOON
WATER

6 LETTERS
DISHES
GREASE
LATHER
LIQUID
SAUCER

7 LETTERS
BUBBLES
CUTLERY
SOAKING

8 LETTERS
DISSOLVE
DRAINERS
TEA TOWEL

9 LETTERS
DISHCLOTH
WASHING UP

G L E A M

OCCUPATIONAL

3 LETTERS
ACE
REP
SPY
TAR
VET
WIG

5 LETTERS
ABBOT
ACTOR
BOXER
COACH
ELDER
ENVOY
MASON
PILOT
PIPER
QUACK
RABBI
SMITH
SPARK
TUNER

6 LETTERS
ARTIST
EXPERT
FLYMAN
GROCER
PASTOR
PEDLAR
PORTER
SLEUTH
TRADER
WRIGHT

7 LETTERS
ACTUARY
CLEANER
COWHERD
DRAYMAN
SERVANT
SURGEON
TEACHER

P
E
D
L
A
R

ALL TALK

3 LETTERS
ASK
BOO
GAB
GAG
HUM
JAW
LIE
MOO
ODE
SAY

4 LETTERS
AVER
AVOW
CALL
ECHO
HOOT
HOWL
LISP
RANT
RAVE

5 LETTERS
AMENS
ARGUE
CHEER
COMIC
EXTOL
GRIPE
HELLO
REPLY
SHOUT
SHUSH
SPOKE
SWEAR
TWANG
VOICE
WINDY

6 LETTERS
BLURTS
CHIRPS
CHORUS
CLUCKS
DIRECT
MANTRA
RECITE
SPEECH
TITTER
YAK-YAK

7 LETTERS
DISCUSS
EPITAPH
EXPRESS
LECTURE
PALAVER
PRATTLE
PURRING
STAMMER
TALKING

8 LETTERS
BERATING
CONVERSE
LANGUAGE
ORDERING
RELATING
RESPONSE

9 LETTERS
JABBERING
VERBALIZE

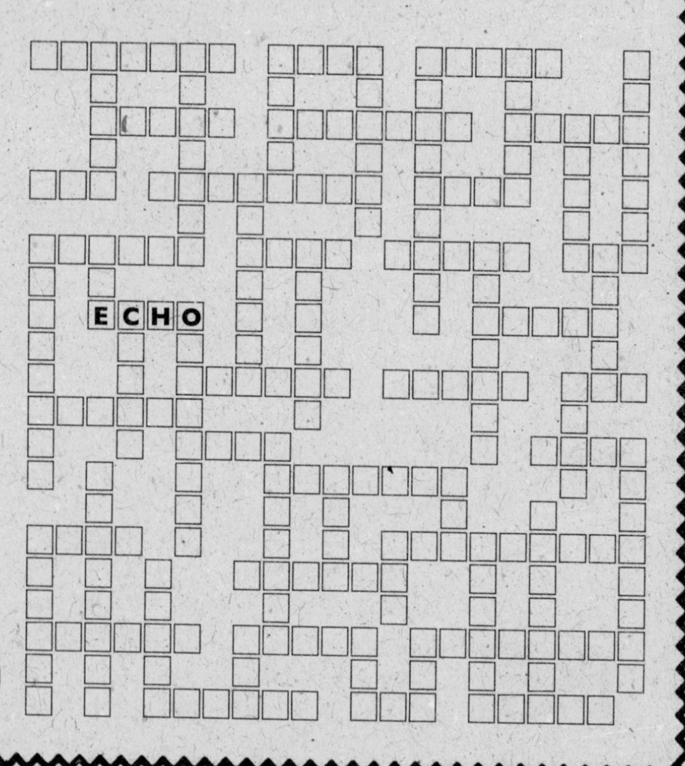

MARATHON RUN

3 LETTERS
HOT
MEN
RUN

4 LETTERS
FAST
LEAD
PACE
RACE
ROAD
TIME
TIRE
VEST

5 LETTERS
CHASE
CLOSE
FIRST
GROUP
MILES
ROUTE
SPEED
START
SUNNY
SWEAT
THIRD
WOMEN

6 LETTERS
CLOUDY
FINISH
LEADER
RECORD
SECOND
SHORTS
SPRINT
WINNER

7 LETTERS
WEATHER

8 LETTERS
ATHLETIC
DISTANCE
MARATHON
TRAINING

10 LETTERS
COMPETITOR

FLOWERING

3 LETTERS
MAY

4 LETTERS
ALOE
ARUM
BALM
FLAG
LILY
MUSK
ROSE
WHIN

5 LETTERS
ASTER
BRIAR
BROOM
CANNA
HENNA
PANSY
POKER
SEPAL
TANSY
TULIP
VIOLA
YUCCA

6 LETTERS
CLOVER
CROCUS
MIMOSA
ROCKET
VIOLET
WATTLE

7 LETTERS
BEGONIA
LOBELIA
PETUNIA
PRIMULA

8 LETTERS
BLUEBELL
LAVENDER
PRIMROSE

9 LETTERS
CARNATION
EDELWEISS

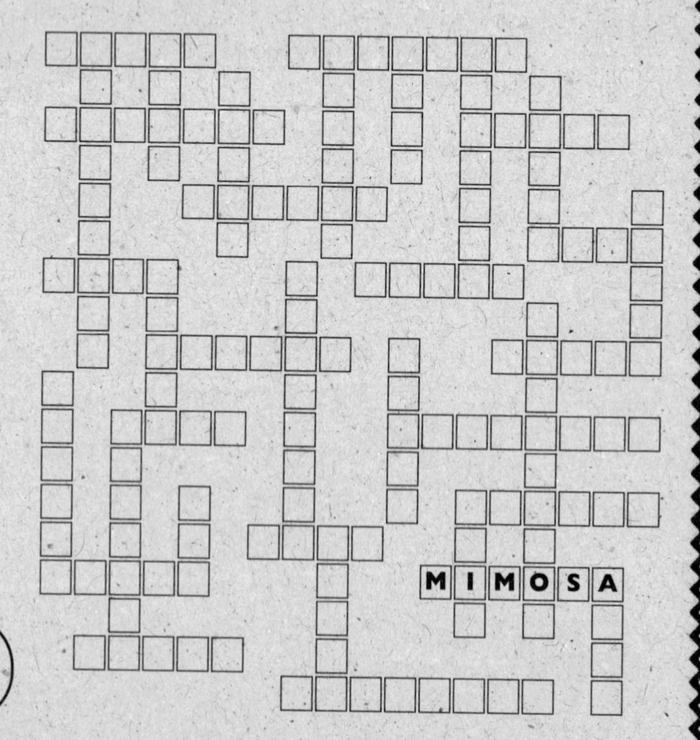

CLUELESS

Fit the words in the grid, then make an answer to the clue in the shaded squares.

Shaded clue: U.K. River.

4 LETTERS
ARID
COMB
EASE
RAMP
SEMI
TART

5 LETTERS
ASIDE
CATER
FAIRY
OCCUR
PASTE
STARS

6 LETTERS
EAGLES
EDITOR
FOREST
HEATER
SAMPLE
TEASED

7 LETTERS
ATHLETE
EATABLE
IGNORED
RESTING

8 LETTERS
EARMUFFS
MAGNETIC

9 LETTERS
AGREEABLE
GATHERING

10 LETTERS
EUCALYPTUS
TRADITIONS

11 LETTERS
IRONMONGERY

IN THE COUNTRY

3 LETTERS
COW
INN

4 LETTERS
BARN
BULL
CORN
GATE
HILL
PATH
SHOP

5 LETTERS
BENCH
CROPS
FENCE
FIELD
GRASS
GREEN
HEDGE
LAMBS
LANES
SHEEP
SPIRE
STILE
TREES

6 LETTERS
CATTLE
CHURCH
FARMER
FLOWER

7 LETTERS
COTTAGE
COUNTRY
SCENERY
STEEPLE
TRACTOR
VILLAGE

8 LETTERS
FOOTPATH
SHEEPDOG
WINDMILL

9 LETTERS
SCARECROW

CAFE CALL

3 LETTERS
CUP
JAM
TEA

4 LETTERS
CAKE
DISH
FORK
MEAL
MENU
MILK
ROLL
SALT
SOUP

5 LETTERS
BREAD
CHAIR
CHIPS
CREAM
DINER
DRINK
JELLY
KNIFE
LUNCH
PLATE
SCONE
SPOON
SUGAR
TABLE
TOAST

6 LETTERS
BUTTER
DINNER
ECLAIR
NAPKIN
PASTRY
PEPPER
SAUCER
TEAPOT

7 LETTERS
BISCUIT

8 LETTERS
CREAM TEA
DOUGHNUT

10 LETTERS
TABLECLOTH

HOT & COLD

3 LETTERS
AIR
DRY
ICY
RAY
WET

4 LETTERS
GUST
HAIL
HEAT
HOAR
RAIN
RIME
SNOW
THAW
WARM
WEST

5 LETTERS
CLOUD
LOWER
MUGGY
SLEET
WINDY

6 LETTERS
AURORA
BREEZE
CHILLY
DEGREE
HOTTER
NIMBUS

7 LETTERS
ELEMENT
ICE-COLD
RAINBOW
RAINING
TEMPEST
THUNDER
TORNADO
TYPHOON
WASHOUT
WEATHER

T H U N D E R

KEEP COMPOSED

4 LETTERS
BERG

5 LETTERS
BIZET
ELGAR
GLUCK
GRIEG
LISZT
RAVEL
SATIE
VERDI

6 LETTERS
BARTOK
CHOPIN
DELIUS
DUSSEK
MOZART
WAGNER

7 LETTERS
CORELLI
DEBUSSY
PUCCINI
PURCELL
STRAUSS
TAVENER
VIVALDI

8 LETTERS
SCHUMANN

9 LETTERS
BEETHOVEN
SCARLATTI

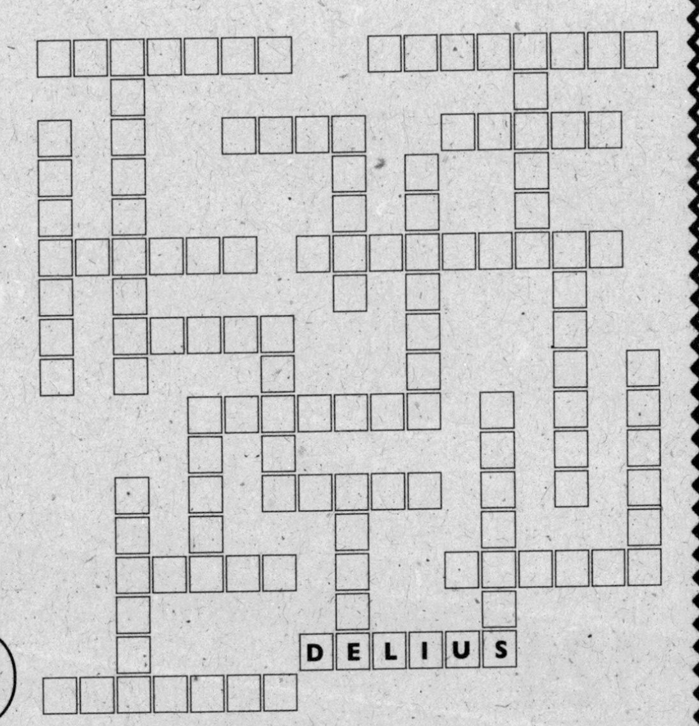

SWEET DREAMS

3 LETTERS
BED
LAY

4 LETTERS
DARK
GOWN
REST
ROBE
SILK
SOFT
TOSS
TURN
YAWN

5 LETTERS
AWAKE
COCOA
COUNT
DREAM
DRINK
NIGHT
QUILT
RELAX
SHEEP
SLEEP
SNORE
TIRED

6 LETTERS
DOUBLE
SHEETS
SINGLE
SLEEPY
WAKE UP

7 LETTERS
BEDROOM
PYJAMAS
SPRINGS
UNDRESS

8 LETTERS
BLANKETS
COVERLET
MATTRESS

9 LETTERS
NIGHTMARE

10 LETTERS
FOUR-POSTER
PILLOW CASE

D R E A M

FRIGHT NIGHT

Fit the words associated with Halloween into the grid.

3 LETTERS
ICY
FLY

4 LETTERS
BREW
CAST
FORM
GLOW
LAMP
MIST
SOUL

5 LETTERS
EERIE
FANGS
GHOST
GHOUL
HAUNT
SCARE
SHAPE
TREAT
TRICK
WEIRD
WITCH

6 LETTERS
CANDLE
FRIGHT
SPELLS
SPIRIT
SPOOKY

7 LETTERS
EVENING
LANTERN
MYSTIFY
SPECTRE

8 LETTERS
CAULDRON
FULL MOON
PUMPKINS

9 LETTERS
HALLOWEEN

10 LETTERS
BROOMSTICK

11 LETTERS
THIRTY-FIRST

T R I C K

CITY VISIT

3 LETTERS
BAR
EAT

4 LETTERS
CITY
SHOW
TAXI
TOWN
TRIP
WALK

5 LETTERS
BREAK
ENJOY
HOTEL
LUNCH
RELAX
RIVER
VIEWS

6 LETTERS
BROWSE
CINEMA
COFFEE
DINNER
EAT OUT
SIGHTS
TRAVEL

7 LETTERS
CONCERT
FRIENDS
GALLERY
STATION
THEATRE

8 LETTERS
SHOPPING

9 LETTERS
BOUTIQUES
CATHEDRAL

10 LETTERS
RESTAURANT

SEASIDERS

4 LETTERS
BUSY
CREW
EELS
RUSH

5 LETTERS
CLAMS
CRABS
HAILS
HOVER
KEDGE
MISTS
PLUMB
RELIC

6 LETTERS
ANCHOR
MULLET
PRAWNS
SCAMPI
TURBOT
WHELKS

7 LETTERS
ADMIRAL
BARQUES
OVERAWE
RESORTS
SEA BASS
SEA LION
SNAPPER
SOCKEYE
STEERED
VESSELS

8 LETTERS
DOLPHINS
EARSHELL
FISH-STEW
HERRINGS
SEASONAL
TRAWLERS

9 LETTERS
BLUE WHALE
DOVER SOLE
IONIAN SEA
PILCHARDS
SHRIMPING

10 LETTERS
CUTTLEFISH
LUMPSUCKER

11 LETTERS
MOUNTAINOUS
THE NAUTILUS

12 LETTERS
BASKING SHARK

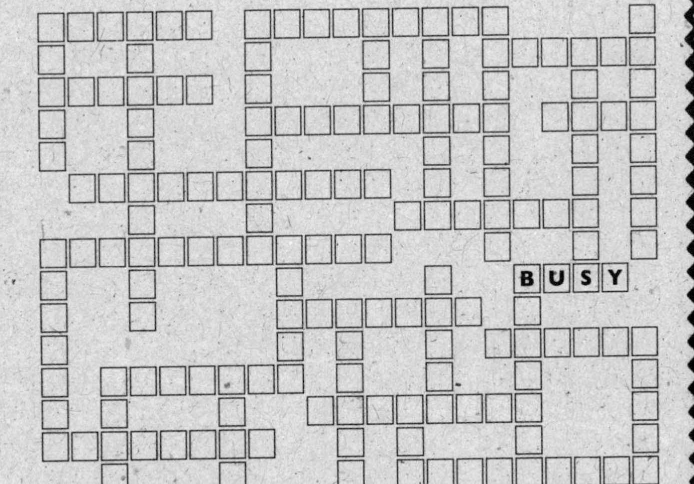

SNOOKERED

3 LETTERS
CUE
POT

4 LETTERS
BALL
DOWN
GAME
NEXT
PINK
REDS
REST

5 LETTERS
BAIZE
BLACK
BREAK
BROWN
ERROR
FINAL
GREEN
ORDER
SCORE
TABLE
WHITE

6 LETTERS
POCKET
WINNER
YELLOW

7 LETTERS
CUSHION
PLAYERS
SESSION
SNOOKER

8 LETTERS
CHAMPION
INTERVAL

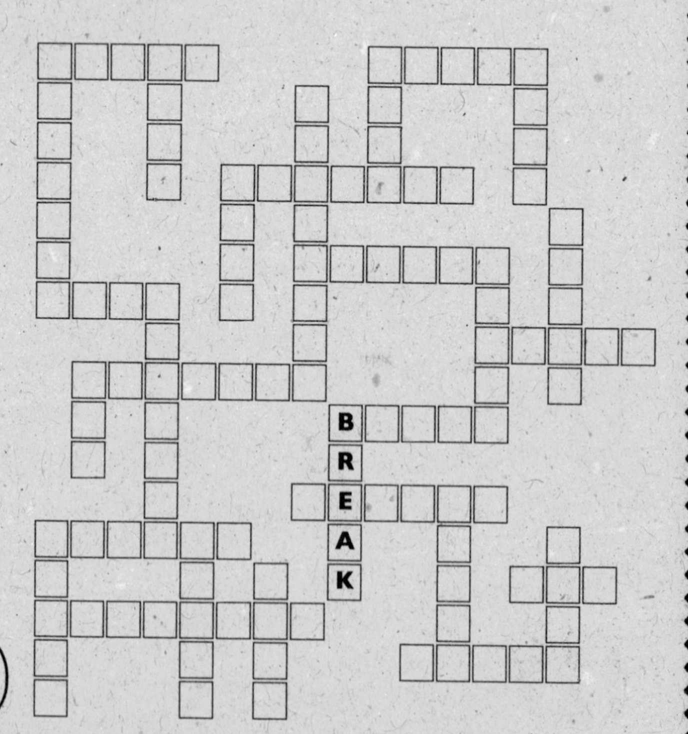

BABY TALK

3 LETTERS
BOY
COT
CRY
OIL
TOY

4 LETTERS
BABY
BATH
GIRL
GRIN
KIDS
LAID
MILK
PLAY
PRAM
TALK
VEST
WAKE
WALK
WASH

5 LETTERS
BIRTH
CRAWL
DUMMY
HAPPY
LAUGH
NAPPY
SLEEP
SMILE
TOWEL

6 LETTERS
BOTTLE
POWDER
RATTLE
WEIGHT

7 LETTERS
BOOTEES
FEEDING
HEALTHY
LAYETTE
LULLABY
MITTENS
NURSERY
TEETHED

9 LETTERS
HIGH CHAIR

T
O
W
E
L

MOTORWAY JAM

3 LETTERS
CAR
FOG
MAP
VAN

4 LETTERS
BEND
EXIT
FAST
HILL
JAMS
JOIN
LANE
PARK
RIDE
ROAD
SLOW

5 LETTERS
ARROW
CLEAR
COACH
LEAVE
LIMIT
PHONE
SIGNS
SPEED
VERGE

6 LETTERS
DRIVER
PETROL
SIGNAL

7 LETTERS
STEERED
TRAFFIC

8 LETTERS
DISTANCE
JUNCTION
OVERTAKE
SLIP ROAD
VEHICLES

11 LETTERS
ORBITAL ROAD
OUTSIDE LANE
SERVICE AREA

S P E E D

AN ACTOR'S LIFE

3 LETTERS
CUE
FAN
HIT
REP
SET
SHY

4 LETTERS
DUET
EPIC
EXIT
FLAT
FLOP
FOIL
HERO
IDOL
JEER
MASK
PACE
PROP
ROLE
SHOW
SKIT
SOLO
STAR
WING

5 LETTERS
ACTOR
ASIDE
COMIC
DECOR
FLOOR
FOYER
HAVOC
HOUSE
SCENE
STAGE
STALL
STUNT
USHER

6 LETTERS
FASTEN
PODIUM
SKETCH
TALENT

7 LETTERS
AMATEUR
CLASSIC
DEADPAN
PRESENT

A C T O R

JUST JOKING

3 LETTERS
ACE
ACT
CAP
KID
TAG

4 LETTERS
GAGS
GLEE
GOOD
JEST
KICK
NUTS
PAYS
ROMP
WISH
WORD
YARN

5 LETTERS
ANTIC
CHEER
CLAPS
DOTTY
FOLLY
INANE
JOLLY
KNACK
LIFTS
MIRTH
PRANK
PUNCH
QUIPS
QUIRK
SCAMP
SILLY
SMILE
SPOOF
TEASE
TRICK

6 LETTERS
COMEDY
GAMBOL
PARODY
PLEASE
TICKLE

7 LETTERS
PARADES
SCREAMS
SNICKER

8 LETTERS
ESCAPADE
LAUGHTER
MISCHIEF
NONSENSE
SPORTIVE

9 LETTERS
CHICANERY
HORSEPLAY
LUDICROUS

CLASS ACT

3 LETTERS
ART
INK
NIB
PEN
SIR
SIT

4 LETTERS
DESK
DRAW
KIDS
READ
TERM

5 LETTERS
BOOKS
CHALK
LEARN
RULER
TEACH
WRITE

6 LETTERS
INFANT
LESSON
PENCIL
SCHOOL
SENIOR
SPORTS
TABLES

7 LETTERS
ENGLISH
HISTORY
INKWELL
SCIENCE
SUBJECT
TEACHER

8 LETTERS
ASSEMBLY
CHILDREN
HOMEWORK

9 LETTERS
CLASSROOM
EDUCATION

10 LETTERS
BLACKBOARD
HEADMASTER

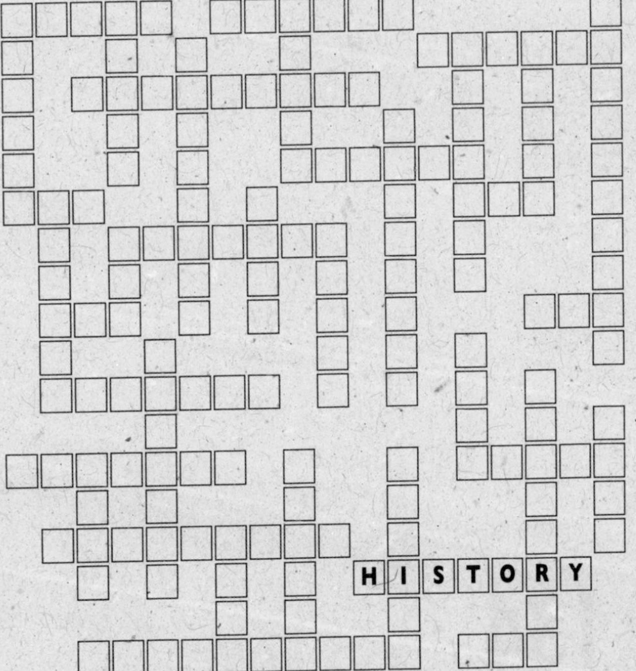

DEVON BOUND

3 LETTERS
BAY
SEA
SIT

4 LETTERS
BOAT
CARS
COVE
PARK
PIER
RAIL
SAND
VIEW
WALK

5 LETTERS
ABBEY
BATHE
BEACH
CLIFF
HILLS
HOTEL
ROADS
SHOPS
TREES
WATER

6 LETTERS
LIGHTS
MARINA
PADDLE
RESORT
TORBAY

7 LETTERS
BRIXHAM
CLIMATE
ENGLISH
GARDENS
HARBOUR
RIVIERA
THEATRE
TORQUAY

8 LETTERS
PAIGNTON

9 LETTERS
BERRY HEAD

10 LETTERS
COCKINGTON

B R I X H A M

TALKING BIG

5 LETTERS
EXTRA
GIANT
GRAND
GROSS
OBESE

6 LETTERS
EXTENT
ROTUND

7 LETTERS
BULBOUS
EXTREME
GOLIATH
HULKING
IMMENSE
LARGEST
LEONINE
MASSIVE
SIZABLE
SWOLLEN
TITANIC

8 LETTERS
ENORMOUS
GIGANTIC
HUGENESS
KING-SIZE
STALWART
TOWERING
WHOPPING

9 LETTERS
CAPACIOUS
EXPANSIVE
MONSTROUS
OVERGROWN
REAL STOUT

10 LETTERS
STUPENDOUS
THUNDERING

11 LETTERS
MAGNANIMOUS
SUBSTANTIAL
VERY FULL TOO

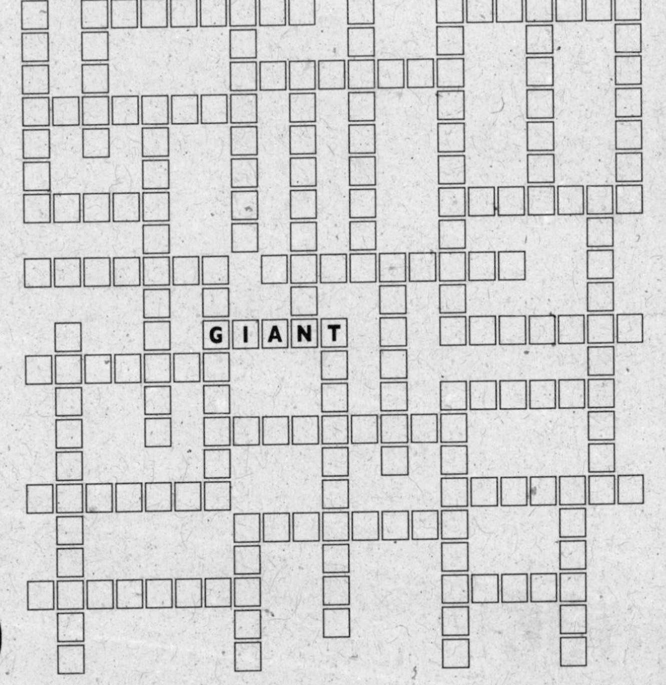

TRAIN LINES

4 LETTERS
COAL
HALT
LINE
MAIL
MEAL
RAIL
SEAT
SLOW

5 LETTERS
COACH
GATES
GUARD
RELAX
STEAM
TRACK
TRAIN
TRIPS

6 LETTERS
BRIDGE
DEPART
DIESEL
DRINKS
DRIVER
ENGINE
POINTS
PORTER
SIGNAL

7 LETTERS
ARRIVED
BRITISH
EXPRESS
VIADUCT

8 LETTERS
GRADIENT
PLATFORM
SLEEPERS
STATIONS

9 LETTERS
TIMETABLE

10 LETTERS
FIRST CLASS

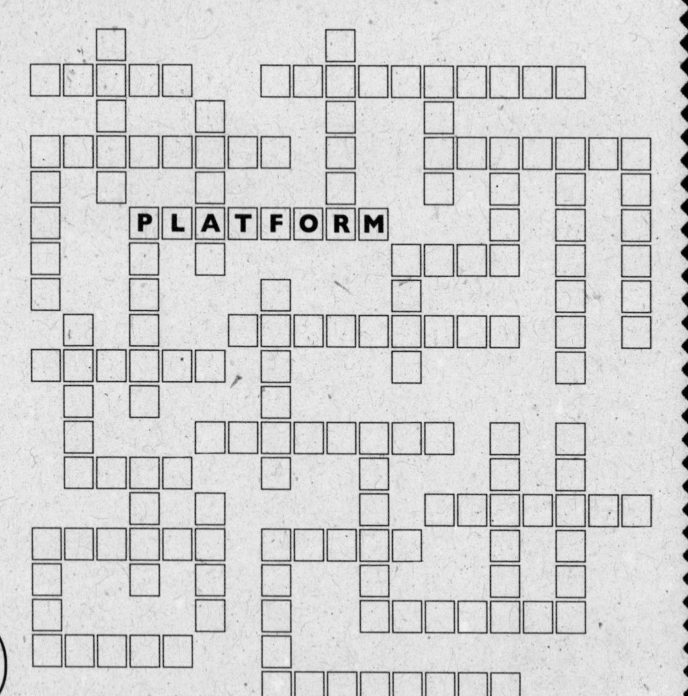

CHESS MOVE

3 LETTERS
PIN

4 LETTERS
DRAW
GAME
KING
MATE
PAWN
PLAY
ROOK
TAKE
TIME
WAIT

5 LETTERS
BLACK
BOARD
CHESS
CLOCK
MOVES
QUEEN
RULES
THINK
WHITE

6 LETTERS
BISHOP
CASTLE
GAMBIT
KNIGHT
PIECES

7 LETTERS
CAPTURE
PROJECT
SQUARES
STUDIED

8 LETTERS
COMPUTER
DIAGONAL
NOTATION
POSITION

9 LETTERS
CHECKMATE

R
O
O
K

SEE THE LIGHT

3 LETTERS
DAY
GAS
LIT
RAY
SEE
SUN

4 LETTERS
BEAM
COAL
FIRE
GLOW
NEON
STAR

5 LETTERS
BLAZE
FLAME
FLARE
FLASH
GLARE
GLEAM
LIGHT
MATCH
SHINE
SUNNY
TAPER
TORCH

6 LETTERS
BEACON
BRIGHT
CANDLE

7 LETTERS
BONFIRE
GLISTEN
LANTERN
RADIANT
SHIMMER

8 LETTERS
DAYLIGHT
ELECTRIC
SPARKLED
SUNLIGHT
SUNSHINE

9 LETTERS
HEADLIGHT

10 LETTERS
ILLUMINATE

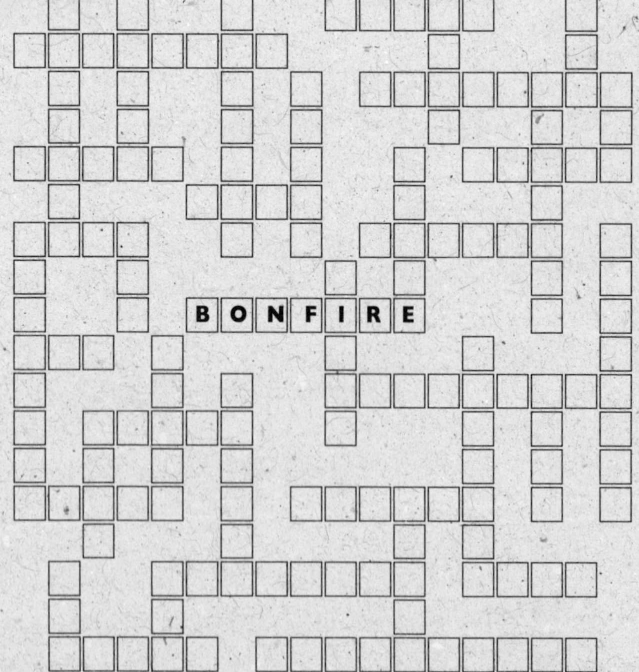

GIRL TALK

3 LETTERS
ANN
IVY
JOY
PAM
UNA

4 LETTERS
ALMA
CLEO
DORA
EMMA
GWEN
JOAN
LILY
LUCY
MARY

5 LETTERS
ALICE
CAROL
DAISY
DIANA
JANET
LAURA
MAUDE
SALLY
SARAH
WENDY

6 LETTERS
ANGELA
DEBBIE
EILEEN
JULIET
SANDRA
SHARON
SYLVIA

7 LETTERS
BARBARA
DOROTHY
MILDRED
PAULINE
VANESSA

8 LETTERS
FLORENCE
JENNIFER
PENELOPE

9 LETTERS
CHRISTINE

L
A
U
R
A

STREET LIFE

Fit the *Coronation Street* words into the grid

3 LETTERS
BET
DEV
JOE
KEN
LES
ROY

4 LETTERS
BETH
CAFE
EMMA
FRED
GAIL
JACK
KIRK
MIKE
RITA
SHOP
VERA

5 LETTERS
BETTY
CURLY
EMILY
JASON
KABIN
KAREN
KEVIN
PETER
ROSIE
SALLY
SARAH
STEVE
TAXIS

6 LETTERS
AUDREY
GARAGE
JANICE
SUNITA
TYRONE

7 LETTERS
DEIRDRE
FACTORY

9 LETTERS
ROYS ROLLS

10 LETTERS
ALLOTMENTS
BOOKMAKERS

12 LETTERS
ROVERS
RETURN

V E R A

CLOTHES ENCOUNTERS

3 LETTERS
HAT
HEM
NAP
TIE

4 LETTERS
BELT
BOOT
MESH
MINI
RAGS
STAY
STUD
TICK
TOPS
WRAP

5 LETTERS
APRON
SHIRT
SHOES
STOLE
TUNIC
TWEED

6 LETTERS
ANGORA
ATTIRE
COLLAR
FABRIC
GALOSH
GARTER
GIRDLE
OUTFIT
RAGLAN
RIBBON
SHORTS
TIGHTS

7 LETTERS
APPAREL
COSTUME
GARMENT
OVERALL
SWEATER
TAFFETA
TWINSET

SWEATER

NOISY

3 LETTERS
BAY
CAW
COO
CRY
MEW

4 LETTERS
BAWL
CALL
ECHO
HOOT
HOWL
LISP
PEAL
PEEP
PURR
RAPS
SIGH
TAPS
TICK
YELL
YELP

5 LETTERS
BARKS
BLARE
CHIME
MOANS
PIPES
PLUMP
PRATE
RINGS
ROARS
SNORE
SNORT
SWISH
WHINE
WHIRR

6 LETTERS
ALARMS
BELLOW
BLASTS
BLEATS
CHEEPS
CHIRPS
CLICKS
MURMUR
RATTLE
RUMBLE
SNEEZE

7 LETTERS
BABBLES
CLATTER
FANFARE
SCREAMS
WHISPER

BLIND DATE

3 LETTERS
HUG
MAN
ONE
TWO
WIN

4 LETTERS
BOYS
KISS
LADS
LOVE
MALE
MEET
PECK
PICK

5 LETTERS
ADORE
CHARM
COURT
GIRLS
ROSES
THREE
WOMAN

6 LETTERS
ANSWER
CHAT UP
CHOOSE
COUPLE
CUDDLE
FEMALE
HUMOUR
LASSES
PRETTY
SCREEN

7 LETTERS
ATTRACT
EMBRACE
PASSION
ROMANCE

8 LETTERS
GORGEOUS
HANDSOME
QUESTION

9 LETTERS
BLIND DATE

10 LETTERS
MATCHMAKER

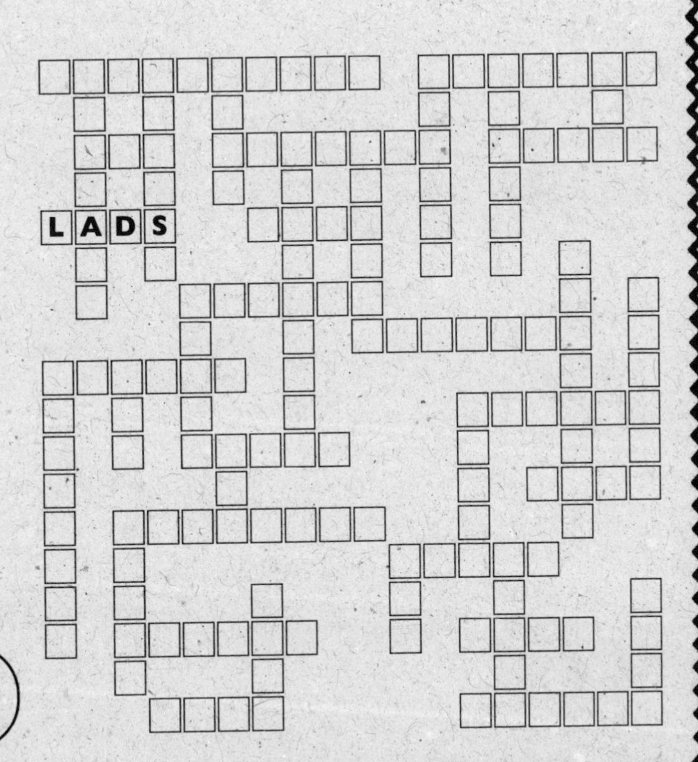

TAKE YOUR TIME

3 LETTERS
AGE
DAY
EON
EVE
NOW

4 LETTERS
DARK
DATE
DAWN
DUSK
ERAS
LENT
NOON
ONCE
PAST
SOON
TERM
WEEK
YEAR
YORE

5 LETTERS
NONCE
OFTEN
SUN-UP
TWICE

6 LETTERS
ANNUAL
DECADE
MINUTE
PERIOD
SECOND
SPRING
SUMMER
SUNDAY
WINTER

7 LETTERS
EARLIER
MOMENTS
MORNING
SUNDOWN

8 LETTERS
DAYBREAK
DECEMBER
MIDNIGHT
THURSDAY

9 LETTERS
AFTERNOON
MANY MOONS
SEPTEMBER
YESTERDAY

10 LETTERS
MAY AND JUNE
MILLENNIUM

DANCE STEPS

3 LETTERS
BOP
HOP
JIG

4 LETTERS
BALL
FEET
JIVE
MOVE
REEL
SPIN
TURN

5 LETTERS
CONGA
DANCE
FLING
POLKA
RONDO
TANGO
TWIST
WHIRL

6 LETTERS
BOLERO
CANCAN
CHA-CHA
CHASSE
GALLOP
MINUET
MORRIS
SHIMMY
TWIRLS
VALETA

7 LETTERS
BEGUINE
ONE-STEP
TWO-STEP

8 LETTERS
HORNPIPE

9 LETTERS
PIROUETTE
POLONAISE

10 LETTERS
CHARLESTON

POT BLACK

3 LETTERS
CUE
POT
TIP

4 LETTERS
BLUE
DRAG
FOUL
KISS
MISS
PINK
REDS
REST
SIDE
SPIN
SPOT

5 LETTERS
BALLS
BLACK
BREAK
BROWN
CLEAN
FRAME
PLANT
SCORE
TABLE
WHITE

6 LETTERS
CANNON
POCKET
SPIDER
YELLOW

7 LETTERS
COLOURS
CUSHION
GLANCED
MAXIMUM
REFEREE
SNOOKER

8 LETTERS
TRIANGLE

9 LETTERS
BAULK LINE

COLOUR FULL

4 LETTERS
FAWN
GOLD
GREY
LIME
PALE
TEAK

5 LETTERS
AZURE
BEIGE
BLOOM
BROWN
CREAM
FLAME
FLESH
FUDGE
GREEN
HENNA
KHAKI
LILAC
MAPLE
MAUVE
RUDDY
SEPIA
STEEL
THEME
UMBER
WHITE

6 LETTERS
DAMASK
MAROON
PASTEL
PEWTER
PURPLE
SILVER
YELLOW

7 LETTERS
MAGENTA

8 LETTERS
BURGUNDY
LAVENDER

SOLUTIONS

PUZZLE 1

	L		T					N					C	H	O	W	
C	A	I	R	N		P	O	O	C	H			O			A	
	B		O					S			P	L	A	Y		T	
	R		T	E	R	R	I	E	R		E		T			C	
	A								U		K					H	
	D	I	N	G	O		K	E	N	N	E	L				D	
	O			R										H		O	
	R		C	O	L	L	I	E					C	O	R	G	I
				W		E						G		U			
				L		A				S	P	R	I	N	G	E	R
			P			S		S				E		D			
	S	H	O	U	G	H		P	U	P	P	Y			S		B
	P		O					I				H			E		A
	A		D			V	E	T			P	O	I	N	T	E	R
	N		L					Z				U			T		K
A	I	R	E	D	A	L	E			C	A	N	I	N	E		I
	E									U		D			R		N
A	L	S	A	T	I	A	N			R							G

PUZZLE 2

		R			F	R	U	I	T					S			
V		U			U							O	R	A	N	G	E
A	L	M	O	N	D									G		A	
N					G					D		P		O		T	
I					E		C	O	C	O	N	U	T			E	
L	E	M	O	N		F				U		D				A	
L		E				L		D		G		D		S	O	U	R
A		L			C	A	K	E		H		I		P			
S	C	O	N	E		N		S		N		N		O		A	
L		N						S		U		G		N		P	
I						S	W	E	E	T				G		P	
C	R	I	S	P	S			R					J	E	L	L	Y
E				E		C		T			E					E	
	T	R	E	A	C	L	E		C		C			I		P	
	A			R		A			R		L			C		I	
	R					R	I	C	E		A		L	I	M	E	
	T	O	F	F	E	E			A		I			N			
						T			M	E	R	I	N	G	U	E	

PUZZLE 3

H	O	C	K	E	Y						B	O	U	N	T	Y
	V		E			G					A				Y	
	E		Y		G	R	A	N	D	L	Y				R	
	R					E			A				E		A	
U	T	I	L	I	T	Y		P	L	A	Y		N		N	
	L			N					L			S	T	O	N	Y
	Y			J	E	R	S	E	Y				I		Y	
F				U			U						T			
U				R			R		S	N	O	W	Y		I	
S	H	I	N	Y			G		E						V	
S			A		A		E		V	I	C	E	R	O	Y	
Y			U		N		R		E		O			R		E
	M	O	G	G	Y		Y		N		O			D		B
	A		H			D			T		K			E		O
	L		T	E	N	A	N	C	Y		E			R		N
M	A	N	Y			Y		R			R	E	A	L	L	Y
	Y							Y			Y			Y		

PUZZLE 4

P	L	U	S						T	A	C	K	L	E
L			P	A	C	K	A	G	E		A			N
A			E		A				N		R			D
Y			A	T	T	E	M	P	T	I	N	G		U
I			K		N		I				I			R
N					A		C			E	V	A	D	E
G	O	S	S	I	P	E	R	S			A			
		E					O			P	L	A	N	T
		A					F					C		
C	O	M	B	S			I					H		
			E			P	L	U	M	P	N	E	S	S
R	A	C	E	D			M		O					T
E			T				E		M		E			E
L		F	R	I	E	N	D	L	E	S	S			E
I			O		P				N		S			P
C			O		I	N	E	R	T	I	A			L
S	T	A	T	I	C						Y	O	K	E

Planet: Pluto.

PUZZLE 5

P	A	S	S		T		P	R	O	W	L		R	O	A	M		
A			K		O		A				O		U			A		
U		W	A	N	D	E	R		R		L	I	N	G	E	R		P
S			T		D		K	N	E	E	L					C		E
E	D	G	E		L				S				A	N	C	H	O	R
		L		D	E	P	A	R	T						A			A
		I		W		A		E					S	T	R	E	A	M
D	O	D	G	E		T		P	U	L	L	U	P		E			B
R		E		L		R		O		I			E		E			U
I				L		O		S		G			E		R	O	L	L
F		T				L	I	E		H	O	L	D					A
T	R	A	V	E	L	S				T		O		C	O	A	S	T
		R					M			S		I		R				E
		R	A	M	B	L	E		B			T	O	U	R	S		
F	L	Y		O			A	R	R	I	V	E		I			S	
L				O			N		O			R		S	T	A	L	L
I				R	A	I	D		O			S		E			I	
T	R	I	P	S			E		D					S	C	U	D	
S							R	E	S	I	D	E	S				E	

PUZZLE 6

P	I	N	T	S	I	Z	E	D			W	E	E			
E											E					M
T	I	N	Y					H	U	G	E			G		I
I				M	I	N	I				N			R		N
T		C					T	I	C	H	Y			E		U
E	N	O	R	M	O	U	S					M		A		T
		L					Y				L	I	T	T	L	E
		O					B		M			N			A	
V	A	S	T			G	I	G	A	N	T	I	C		R	
		S					T		M			A			G	
S	M	A	L	L			S		M			T			E	
L		L					Y		O			U		P		
I									T			R		U		
G	I	A	N	T					H		T	E	E	N	Y	
H					B									Y		
T	I	T	A	N	I	C										
					G											

PUZZLE 7

	F					B	R	O	C	C	O	L	I				I
	I		C			O				R							N
C	L	E	A	R		W		C		O		H	E	A	T		S
	L		R			L		U		U		O			H		T
	I		R					P	O	T	A	T	O		I		A
E	N	J	O	Y			F			O					C	A	N
	G		T		T		L			N		L	E	E	K		T
		A	S	P	A	R	A	G	U	S		E					
					S		V				O	N	I	O	N	S	
M	I	N	E	S	T	R	O	N	E			T				P	
U					Y		U					I		S	T	I	R
S		P	E	A			R					L		P		C	
H		A							P	A	N			O		Y	
R	I	C	H			B				R				O			
O		K		H	E	R	B		C	O	N	D	E	N	S	E	D
O		E				O				M					O		
M		T	O	M	A	T	O			A			P	O	U	R	
						H									P		

PUZZLE 8

O	R	C	H	E	S	T	R	A		P	L	E	C	T	R	U	M
P		Y				R				I			H				A
E		M	A	N	D	O	L	A		A		V	I	O	L	I	N
R		B				M				N			M				D
A		A				B	A	N	J	O			E		G		O
S	O	L	O			O		O			B	A	S	S	O		L
		S				N		T	U	B	A				N		I
			F	I	F	E		E			S		O	R	G	A	N
V	I	O	L		O						S		B				
I			U		R		P	I	C	C	O	L	O		B		B
O			T	I	M	E					O		E	T	U	D	E
L	U	T	E					H	O	R	N				G		L
A		A						A							L		L
		B	A	S	S			R		Q	U	A	R	T	E	T	S
D	U	O			A			M					E			H	
U		R			X	Y	L	O	P	H	O	N	E			E	
E		E						N					D	R	U	M	
T	A	T	T	O	O		S	Y	M	B	O	L	S			E	

PUZZLE 9

				S		R		J	E	T				B		G
S	O	L	I	T	A	I	R	E					J	A	D	E
				O		N		W		B		P		N		M
				N		G		E	A	R	R	I	N	G		S
L	O	C	K	E	T			L		O		N		L		
A		H			O			S		O			B	E	A	D
P		O		O	P	A	L			C			R			I
I		K			A					H			A			A
S		E			Z		P						C			M
N		R		R			E			C	A	M	E	O		O
E				U			N			H			L			N
C				B			D		P	A	S	T	E			D
K		C	R	Y	S	T	A	L		R			T			
L		L					N			M						
A		A		A	M	E	T	H	Y	S	T					
C		S														
E		P	E	A	R	L	N	E	C	K	L	A	C	E		

PUZZLE 10

			G								T	A	L	K		W	
	T	R	I	C	K	S			P		U			I	C	E	S
	E		R					D	R	I	N	K		D		L	
B	A	L	L	O	O	N	S		E		E			S		C	
I		E							S							O	
R		M				C	A	K	E			C	R	E	A	M	
T		O		S		H			N			A				E	
H		N		W	R	A	P		T		F	R	U	I	T		B
D		A	G	E		I						D		C			L
A		D		E		R		G	A	M	E	S		E			O
Y		E	A	T		S		I						C	H	E	W
				S				F	O	O	D			R			
						H	A	T			E		J	E	L	L	Y
I				G		A					S			A		J	
C		C	R	I	S	P	S		B		S			M		G	
I				V		P		L	O	V	E					H	
N	O	I	S	E		Y			Y		R		P	A	R	T	Y
G											T						

PUZZLE 11

			F						F	I	F	T	Y				
	T	H	O	U	S	A	N	D				H		M	A	N	Y
	W		U		I					E		I		O			
F	O	U	R		X					L		R		R			
			T		T	W	E	L	V	E		T	W	E	N	T	Y
N	O	N	E		E					V		E					
	N		E		E				S	E	V	E	N	T	E	E	N
	E		N	I	N	E	T	E	E	N		N		H			
									V					R			
				E			T		E	I	G	H	T	E	E	N	
	Z		M	I	L	L	I	O	N					E		U	
F	E	W		G			M									M	
	R			H		L	E	S	S		H	U	N	D	R	E	D
C	O	U	N	T			S						U			R	
			I										M		L	O	W
			N	I	L				S				B			U	
			E		O			F	I	F	T	E	E	N		S	
					T	E	N		X				R				

PUZZLE 12

B	L	O	O	M	E	R			O	F	F	B	E	A	M	
L				I								O				
U		M	I	S	U	N	D	E	R	S	T	O	O	D		
N				T				R				B			U	
D		C	L	A	N	G	E	R		G	O	O	F		N	
E		O		K				O				O			T	
R		N		E			W	R	O	N	G			E	R	R
		F						S			A		S		U	
		U									F	A	L	S	E	
		S				H					F		I			
		E			N	O	T	T	R	U	E		P		M	
	U					W							U		I	
	N					L			F	A	U	X	P	A	S	
	J					E			O						L	
	U	N	F	A	I	R		S	L	I	P				E	
	S								L						A	
	T			F	A	U	L	T	Y						D	

SOLUTIONS

PUZZLE 13

EPSOM FLIGHT AMOUNT
Y O E O A Y
E U E P S R
BUSINESS DEFEAT A
R K T T E N N
O I ADJUSTMENT LIFT
W L I M O E R
SKIING B U INCOMES
F R LARK N S
JETPLANE IDEALS H
U I D T I E
M T EXALTED TONE
PRICES L O O R
I H O W U DAUBER
S F EBB I E
HELICOPTER THRUST G
I E A C E T A
L A V H A I R
LADDER ROCKET TREND

PUZZLE 14

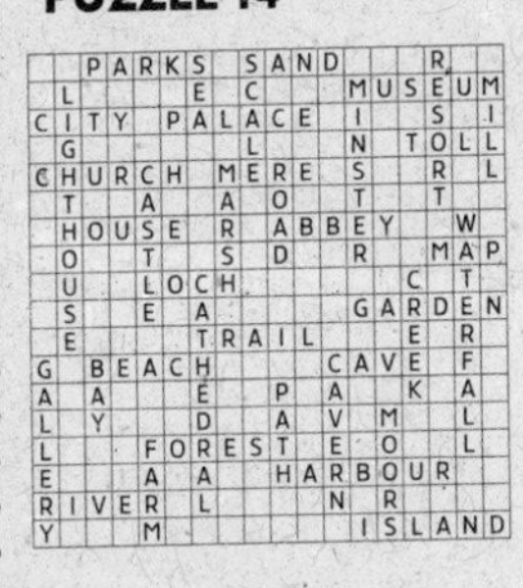

PARKS SAND R
L E C MUSEUM
CITY PALACE I S I
G L N TOLL
CHURCH MERE S R L
T A A O T T
HOUSE R ABBEY W
O T S D R MAP
U LOCH C T
S E A GARDEN
E TRAIL E R
G BEACH CAVE F
A A E P A K A
L Y D A V M L
L FOREST E O L
E A A HARBOUR
RIVER L N R
Y M ISLAND

PUZZLE 15

G GARAGE GORGE
GATHER A O A
A A A GORGON GROG
G N C O R GIN R
GREATEST U G A A
I GLEE GRAND
N G GAG O O L U
GOADER R U R G A
I I E S GARMENT
N GNAW I E E
GAS A GREASE GAD
I L GOO N T R
G GAVEL I GIVING
G A A I N G N L U
L U N D GEAR GALES
I GRIME S A S A T
N E S R O T GEE
GASPED GNOMELIKE D

PUZZLE 16

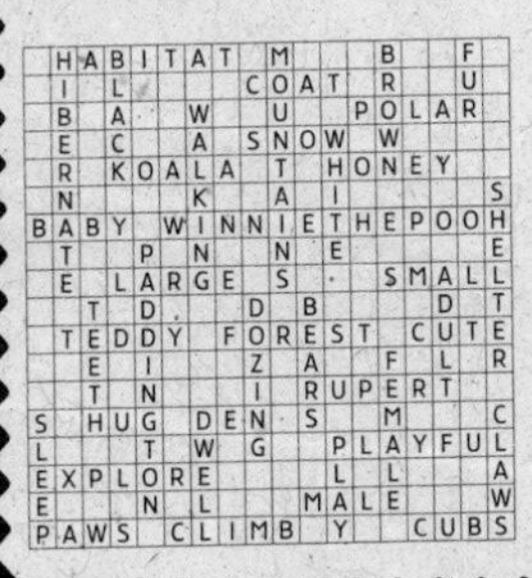

HABITAT M B F
I L COAT R U
B A W U POLAR
E C A SNOW W
R KOALA T HONEY
N K A I S
BABY WINNIETHEPOOH
T P N N E E
E LARGE S SMALL
T D D B D T
TEDDY FOREST CUTE
E I Z A F L R
T N I RUPERT
S HUG DEN S M C
L T W G PLAYFUL
EXPLORE L L A
E N L MALE W
PAWS CLIMB Y CUBS

PUZZLE 17

GIN B C WARM
L I ROUND P L
A L T F WINE
STOUT FOOD N
S C E E R K T
A REFRESHING O
PULL A N INN
U TABLE K N I
MILD E COSY
P A CHEERS P
G H R E S S I
E A R H H R
BAR I VILLAGE I
R FROTH E N R T
A P S I S CIDERS
N I M N H Y Y
DINE MENU A
Y T G TALK

PUZZLE 18

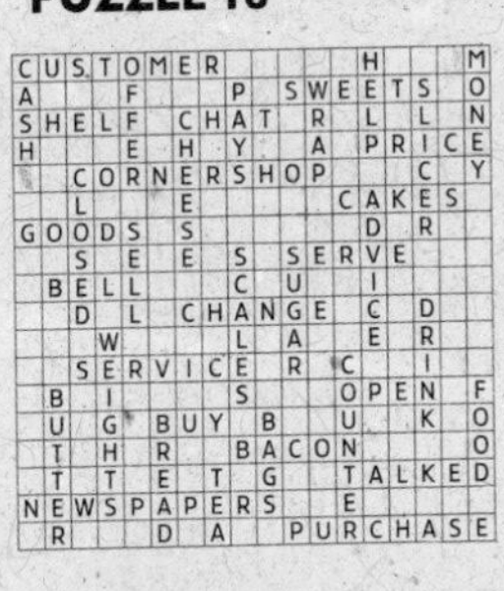

CUSTOMER H M
A F P SWEETS O
SHELF CHAT R L L N
H E H Y A PRICE
CORNERSHOP C Y
L E CAKES
GOODS S D R
S E E S SERVE
BELL C U I
D L CHANGE C D
W L A E R
SERVICE R C I
B I S OPEN F
U G BUY B U K O
T H R BACON O
T T E T G TALKED
NEWSPAPERS E
R D A PURCHASE

PUZZLE 19

P E
CLUTCH START E
A S O T
FIRST WHEEL WIPERS
N C O
D DASHBOARD BELT
I O P N I G O
CHOKE D D A N
A R E T GEAR N W
T D Y A E I
N O R LIGHTS N
E REVERSE B E E D
U N A STOP MATS
T G D O B T C
RADIO I ROTORARM R
A N A O I A K E
L KEY TRAVEL K E
O D E FAN
DRIVER S PLUGS

PUZZLE 20

INFLUENCE EXCEL TACT
L C S R C O I
L H R L T E RESPECT
U E E AWARDS L S L
STAR SPOT T I E R E
T D U E TRIBUTE
R FORTUNE R A S
I O A L D JACKPOT
O GREAT RICHES T A
U C I T A E COST
S E O EXALTED R U
N P S R BONUS
PRAISE R S A W
O A PROSPERITY NEWS
I F O P T N U
SUCCESS E W O R
E A R I E R AFFLUENCE
R T TEAM F
SECURITY L EMINENCE
E O T C
WORTH N ACHIEVEMENT

PUZZLE 21

COASTER D
L B PONTOON
MOTORBOAT A R
O A R N Y L
Y P R Q SMACK I
A G U C E S F
CANOE E U CORACLE
H L O B
STEAMER LINER W O
R S F A
S KETCH G C RAFT
C R I O U E
DHOW I PUNT T I D
O M D TUG I
ROWBOAT COBLE H N
N R L R T G
E BOAT YAWL E H
R N FERRY

PUZZLE 22

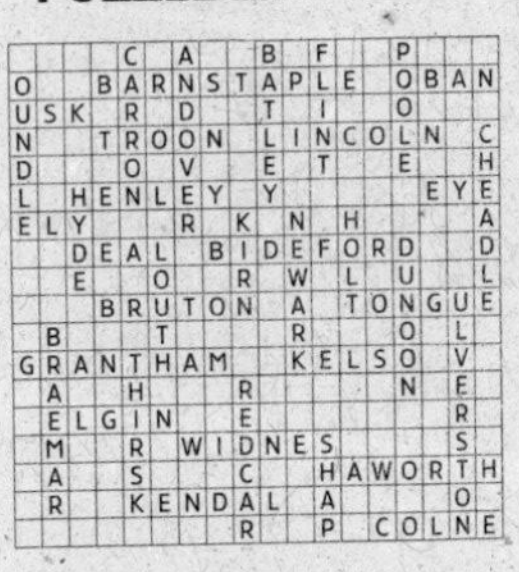

C A B F P
O BARNSTAPLE OBAN
USK R D T I O
N TROON LINCOLN C
D O V E T E H
L HENLEY Y EYE
ELY R K N H A
DEAL BIDEFORD D
E O R W L U L
BRUTON A TONGUE
B T R O L
GRANTHAM KELSO V
A H R N E
ELGIN E R
M R WIDNES S
A S C HAWORTH
R KENDAL A O
R P COLNE

PUZZLE 23

MATCHMAKER PASSION
T H E R C N
TWO EMBRACE ROSES
R O T L N T E
LADS KISS T E
C E N W Y N Q
T CUDDLE U C
O D ROMANCE O
HUMOUR A E U
A A R T CHATUP
N N THREE H I L
D U A LOVE
S GORGEOUS R N
O I WOMAN
M R P I D M
E LASSES N BOYS A
S C R L
PICK FEMALE

PUZZLE 24

S L
MIRROR TRAFFIC
E O N A R
H V SPEED R
DRIVER L L
R G R ROUNDABOUT
LIGHTS W E O U
V W E U KERB
E A TUITION N
L TYRES R H L
E C E A P A E
SCHOOL Y LEARN A
S D E S DOOR
O TEST SIGNS B N
N R I E BRAKE
START SIGNAL A R
I H R K
INSTRUCT S STEER

SOLUTIONS

PUZZLE 25

SUGAR STICK
U F I
M PARTICLE
M R O I P
E O O ASIA
RECENT S N
T H O
P A ANIMAL
EGGS C E E
G O H I N
UNIVERSE T
M L I
CREPE PEARL

Sea creature: Porpoise.

PUZZLE 29

C H R J W
ROYALFLUSH O I W
I N N KING H
BRIDGE E A I
B COURT M S
BACCARAT A BEAT
G A N L
HEART SNAP PLAYER
D H S O C E
TWIST SUIT N K D
R T F A T
U S U F D O D
M T R L I O LAID
PATIENCE A N S
C L M DEUCE
JACK FULLHOUSE A
C B N A R
DEALER SPADE LEAD

PUZZLE 33

SOURCE HENLEY B
T I O E
RUNS B G C N
E MOUTH K BROAD
A A O I
MOVE TOWPATH V F
T E E L
R OXFORD MARLOW
TOWN L R O
U O SWIFT F D
G LOW T S WAVES
H O I EBB L S
N CALM A L B H
WIND A L WINDSOR I
A O S K I P
T N THAMES TIDES
E L G
RIPPLE VALLEY

PUZZLE 26

F BLEND H
L R TASTED
A E S B E R
V S WATER A B
SOOTHE I E B LEAF
U R D R WEAK L
BREAK G T S
I S E W
R N S S TASTE
BEVERAGE I E E
F R U CUPPA HOT
R C P E
E CREAM SPOON N
S H R I O T B E
H I PLANT POUR
N D I
STEAM KETTLE

PUZZLE 30

ANIMAL
DRAW C P R
A N S A E T A T W
R I N K R N I N A O
K M E T C SKILL R
CARTOONIST M E D
F T C O L PAINTS
TONE H N S T T
R L F M I
MOVE I COLOURS
A G O N
SHADE U T
T FREEHAND L
Y E R R E I
LIGHT FAST T N
E P S PAPER
LIFELIKE I S
N SCALE

PUZZLE 34

DALMATIAN MOTTLED
A W R A O
SADDLE CONFETTI M
U E R T E I
N SPIDER E O Y N
S P A C MOLE O
PIED P S K A I E
O C MOTH BLOT Z S
T K G E SNAKE
S SPLOTCHES R
I O CARD H
LEOPARD S SITE
S ACES F A
CAP P O LASER
H INKSPOTS E T
A N I L O PEACOCKS
R T L E A K I
TROUT D DOTS SPOTS

PUZZLE 27

TELEVISION SWITCH
R I C C O
A SOFT COLOUR TONE
N T O H N E U T
S E CLEAR T E B R
M N U N RANGE A
I SOUND O S
T R E LOUD T
AERIAL
D S SHARP
DISH WATCH H L
O E I A O U
A E R T R V G
PROGRAMME I BUTTON
I LOOK L B
ADJUST E N PICTURE
E S M A
WAVES SATELLITE M

PUZZLE 31

WILD V O S S W
A HEAVEN UNFIT
ROAR E E O N N
M AIR R WEST T
C SUN ICE P E
I L D T A B O R
R A O H STRATUS
R TEMPEST A
ICY R C LOW
M DRIZZLE I
TORNADO N E A N
B A L W G P S D
R V END HOT Y
I CALM P DRY H
G G I O U RISE
SHINE SQUALL A
T D T R L GUST

PUZZLE 35

PACKETS BAG BREAD
R A R O R
O SUPERMARKET S I
D H N T TINS
U REFUND D L A K
C B I SAVE F
T AISLE G T S FOOD
R L MONEY I
S C O S SOUPS
TROLLEY D C H C
A D S U O B O
CHECKOUT S P U U
K E I B T PAY N
S R L A O I T
VEGETABLES M N W
L A K EGGS I
L L PRICE R N
T SHOPPER

PUZZLE 28

JACQUELINE
A E KAY
M L JOE L LUKE
E O N I Y I
S R LORRAINE T
N R M D H
LAURA O
A LINDA
LARRY KATE J
I O J O
JASON N JACK S
E S A N A E
S A KATHERINE R P
S E D E H
I JULIE LEN I
C O L E N
A Y Y JOLENE

PUZZLE 32

LIGHTNING STORM F S
U S O P A CLAP
L L OILSKIN A L
GALOSHES A N S O
Y P E SLIDE HOT
R ARCH R C
ARCTICS I DONRUSH
O N P I P N
SLICKER PARKAS SOP
L L L E B E
STREAM E SPLATTER
H I U S T I
SLUSH S FLOOD I L N
P N I T R DANGERS
A D PISCES L D I
T E S ICE D N
T R DASH O SPRING
E I E V I L O I
R I P T DOWNPOUR

PUZZLE 36

C CLOCK
BATH H S A T
E E ATTIC ROOMS
D L I A P I O
R E FURNITURE LOFT
O V L R P T E A
O I O C S T
M STOOL A TAPS
I R O S A
DOOR U E I HALL
N LINO RADIO A
G S M M
KITCHEN TILES P
R A
O BED DOWNSTAIRS
O L M V I U
FIREPLACE N LIGHT
T N K

SOLUTIONS

PUZZLE 37

GUM PASTE A
E I N H
PIN M SECURE C O
A D O E H O
P O B PADLOCK
FETTER D I A R A
R E O NAIL N
W T BOND R WELD
E H R E E
I E STITCH D Y
G RIVET H GLUE
H O STAPLE
STICK P I
E HARNESS
M F K
ADHERE FASTENING
N I E I
BUTTON X W BOLT

PUZZLE 41

P TICKETS
LETTER O
N U QUEUE P P
S S BUY N E A
I W B STATIONERY
NOTELET E C
N E R CORD PACKET
T T E L
POSTCARD MONEY
O G E C L
STAMPS N AIRMAIL
T C V L C
POSTALORDER J E
F I L C O INK
FORMS S O A T C
I H PAPER TAPE
C BOOKS E D E
E P STRING

PUZZLE 45

B C CHEERS BEAT
SHERRY X I A I
W A STILTON R
FIZZ B R J I
T ELEGANT OPEN
C E I F G
CHASER DEPART G
L O A S I R
TONIC FUNNY ENJOY
W I L C N P
N PARADE SEDUCE
A L I E L
SPIN RELAXED A
L I O Y ROMP
E FESTIVE I O
E T I E UNRULY
PLAY PAIRED K R

PUZZLE 38

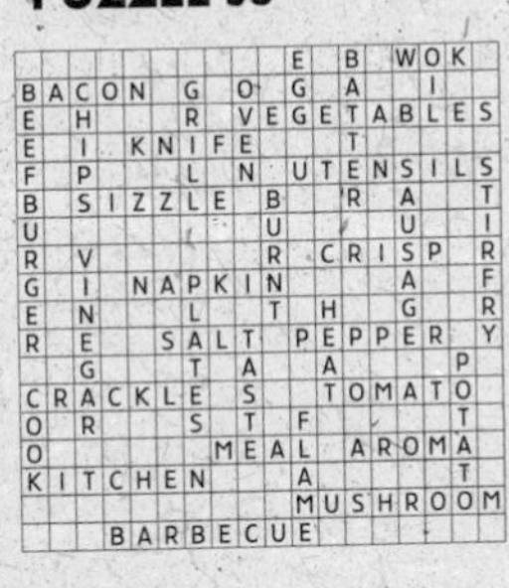

E B WOK
BACON G O G A I
E H R VEGETABLES
E I KNIFE T
F P L N UTENSILS
B SIZZLE B R A T
U U U I
R V R CRISP R
G I NAPKIN A F
E N L T H G R
R E SALT PEPPER Y
G T A A P
CRACKLE S TOMATO
O R S T F T
O MEAL AROMA
KITCHEN A T
MUSHROOM
BARBECUE

PUZZLE 42

STEWARDESS B D
E L PASSENGERS
AVIATION E M L T L
T I E O TYRE E
S T RADIO S N E
CLOUDS T T P
U D ROUGH MOVIES
FOG E C T O
I G ENTER DISTANCE
R A A M M A L
S G R ENGINE K E
TREMBLE L JETS V
C Y TICKET O A
LANDS O O F T
A R C U CREW FAR I
S I A I R K E E O
SIGN R I P READS N
K G SKIES A T
PASSPORT T TENSES

PUZZLE 46

BUBBLY STRONG C
U E H P COLD
R F LABEL E R
GROW R R UNCORK B
U R R E S O
N T DRY FILL C T
DRINK R L FRUIT
Y F M E A E L
VINEYARD TRY WINE
G E T A
L D POUR SIP V
A O R T I
S R E SMELL TANG
SWEET H R T
H CHAMPAGNE A
VINE O R A G
T GRAPES D E
E K

PUZZLE 39

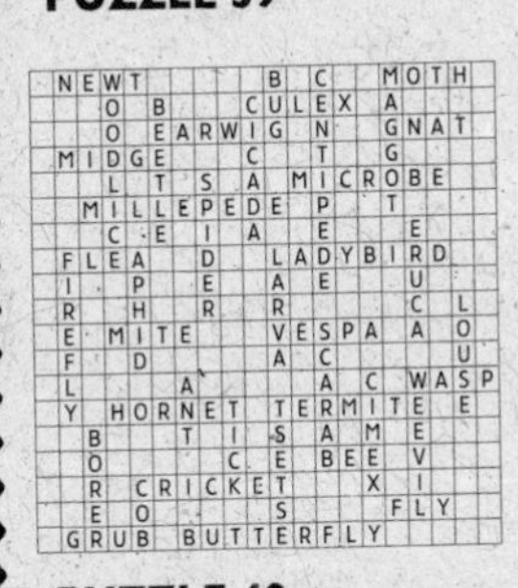

NEWT B C MOTH
O B CULEX A
O EARWIG N GNAT
MIDGE C T G
L T S A MICROBE
MILLEPEDE P T
C E I A E E
FLEA D LADYBIRD
I P E A E U
R H R R C L
E MITE VESPA A O
F D A C U
L A A C WASP
Y HORNET TERMITE E
B T I S A M E
O C E BEE V
R CRICKET X I
E O S FLY
GRUB BUTTERFLY

PUZZLE 43

POTTERY DECORATE B
V H E N U A
EARTHENWARE RACK
N O G M N E
WATER E WHEEL
A L H R
M H V SPIN J
ORNAMENT R K U
U R GILDING
BLENDER E L C
D E FIRING H
V BONE L I
A PORCELAIN
SHAPED A O Z A
E O I DIP L E
T S N O
BOWLS HEAT BUBBLES
R

PUZZLE 47

JAMB G H GARAGE
U DRYROT A U
VASE A T SPICES
I TEAPOT O S
RECIPE L PLENTY
L TOAST I
SPATULA T U S FAN
A P G N EARTH U
WIRE K M KNOB
O BRASS O S G A
PAN O R C IRONING
N DRILL A
SPRING S SPIDER
I E TISSUE U
WARMTH O D OVEN
N O CRAVAT E
COBWEB S N ITEM

PUZZLE 40

TAIL CLIMB
F E L L
FLAP PLAY FOOD
E P L W P R V
C C PAWS U I E
T L Y R E
LITTER F SPRING
O A U K I D L
N INTELLIGENT W I
A O T T G H C
TABBY B T P MILK
E O SIAMESE S I
D W S N R K N
ROLL F K S E G
I U E GINGER
N SCRATCH A SIT
K A N O
WATCH CREAM

PUZZLE 44

CLIFF LEGAL
H E R
A PERSUADE
L L O E B
K C U FLEA
SEASON D I G
N D G
A A LIGHTS
R ASP E T T
C T S S R
PARASITE E
U E E
SLATE SPORT

Sea creature: Lobster.

PUZZLE 48

D T R H H
CHAT A LONELY O
R T L M A A N
E FEMALE A R S E
L R A N TALK S
I INTERESTS L T
A E E O I COMPANY
B N M C N
LADY MEET GENUINE
E O M
K M B P B
F I E TOGETHER
LOVES H E Y O A
N SHORT G N C
D W L I SINCERE
CARED N R I
R GENTLEMAN
HUMOUR G

SOLUTIONS

PUZZLE 49

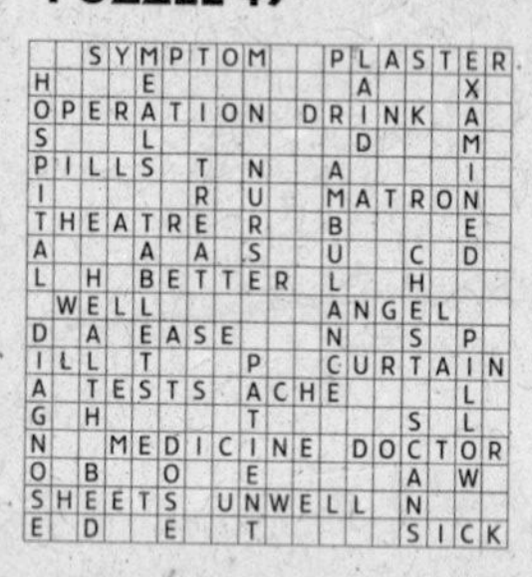

SYMPTOM PLASTER
H E A X
OPERATION DRINK A
S L D M
PILLS T N A I
I R U MATRON
THEATRE R B E
A A A S U C D
L H BETTER L H
WELL ANGEL
D A EASE N S P
I L L T P CURTAIN
A TESTS ACHE L
G H T S L
N MEDICINE DOCTOR
O B O E A W
SHEETS UNWELL N
E D E T SICK

PUZZLE 53

C S F
RETURN WIMBLEDON B
F N M I A I R A
O TOPSPIN SINGLES C
R R I L N H E H K
TIEBREAKER S MATCH
N C E Y R N A
I O D MIXED N
G U S L LOVE D
H RACKET U N
T T O T B C A
T R LADIES O D
E E B E E V V
N GRASS R E A
NET A L SERVER N
I M LAWN E SET
SLICE C L A
E VOLLEYING
B E

PUZZLE 57

SHOWER RADIATOR
P A I
O T N M F
N E S A RELAX
G BRUSHTEETH A
E U T N
BATH CLEAN
B O E
TALC TOWELS COLD
A E P U
P SHAMPOO L C
S I LAZE K
SCRUB S WASH
I R SHAVE
N O O TUB
SOAK R SCALES
P

PUZZLE 50

TELEPHONE POST
Y O S E
P F LETTERS L
EMAIL E M TELEX
W X A C G C
R W SPEAK R A
INTERNET H R MAIL
T A A O D M L
E L T P R N R
R K TELETEXT O E
S E T P
CONTACT I O
W C CARD
W MOBILEPHONE T
E S R A E
BROADCAST T WRITE
S S

PUZZLE 54

MEAL W O C BREW
A O I P H F H
T CONVERSATION I
A E N T O K S
PULL SPIRITS DRINK
O N E D Y
ROUND G R GLASS
N A T L H
LAGER I BOTTLE E
A E T M A R
S SALE R CHAIRS
T B M H Y
ORANGE TABLES B P
R R B I E R L
DOMINOES D R A A
E A E SHANDY
R N SERVE D
S COMPANY

PUZZLE 58

HARP TABLET
A LEARNER L E
M A D O O A
S NAVIGATION S
T T E R M E
E R E FINER
REPARTEES N
E N AGATE
A H C
FORGE O R
R AUTHORESS
DELAY S E A
E D E R Y L
A MICROSCOPE V
R E O I A A
E N ADDICTS G
RENTED TAME

Item of clothing: Vest.

PUZZLE 51

L D SWINE MULE
I O H I L P
VOLE PET O N A A
N D L SKUNK M N
E HIPPO A HART
S N TAPIR H
STAG T I HARE
DONKEY B Y R
KID A RAT A ELK
D A G KITTEN
ORYX H G LAMB
L MOOSE A U
PUMA R RHINO F
H O BEAST O D F
I U U E PUG GOAT
N S L N N L
SEAL PANDA U O

PUZZLE 55

P
CLUTCH START E
A S O T
FIRST WHEEL WIPERS
N C O
D DASHBOARD BELT
I O P N I G O
CHOKE D D A N
A R E T GEAR N W
T D Y A E I
N O R LIGHTS N
E REVERSE B E E D
U N A STOP MATS
T G D O B T C
RADIO I ROTORARM R
A N A O I A E
L KEY TRAVEL K E
O D E FAN
DRIVER S PLUGS

PUZZLE 59

COMPUTER JOB H
I O Y A
R DRIVE SOFTWARE
C E N C E D S
U MONITOR W C
I E E D A A
TYPE R EXIT RUN
R K ON S F E
PROCESS C L S
I G Y PASSWORD Y
X R A P O M
E A L V P W B
L MEMORY E Y N O
G L
T O ERRORS
HACKING A
B RELOAD

PUZZLE 52

LEAF P DATE
I F VALUE I
E R A O A ART
D S I L T L L
I LITERATURE E E O
T O M R R
I N PRINTED S I
OLD A E BINDING
N O G X S G I
INDEX STANDS N N
A S P U E A
U L I COVER D L
T REPRINT E S
H A E JACKET
O V S GILT D C
RARE E I BOOK
SKETCHES N
T BOUND

PUZZLE 56

BUCKET FLAGON VAT N
U A L L E U O
T R SCABBARD S BAG
TEAPOT S S E S G
F O KEGS M E I
SKEP U VIAL CAN
A AMPHORA J S R
U T O O CASK
CREEL L NICHES D
E L CELL N L
PAIL H S SOCKETS
A ALEMBIC A
N G S RECESS U B
CRUET V I T T A
I HAMPERS EWERS
CUP V L R N I
R PANNIER JARS S N
I S S U BINS
BARREL E G L

PUZZLE 60

CRICKET EARWIG H
E A S N O
N BUTTERFLY A R
T Y T A MOTH N
I D S D I E
P SPIDER Y TERMITE
E D F BEE
D G L I W G C
E R FLY DRONE R I
U L D E A C
S BEETLE VESPA
C A O I S D
ANT U L L H A
R WASP O O
A O E C APHID
BORER U P
MANTIS FIREFLY
T R

SOLUTIONS

PUZZLE 61

HAPSBURG DAVID TSAR
A R E T E A U H
R E H N U NICHOLAS
O REGENT P I H R
L R L H N I
DUKE ELIZABETH
A N S A G
HORATIO W MARY
I L T HAILE L A
G SULTAN N V E C
H O O D ESTHER
N P H BESS Q E O
E HELEN L O JUAN Y
S I R EMIR I R A
SOLOMON L ROY L
I JOSEPH E I
EMPIRE O H A ARMS
E D H A URBAN T
AGHAKHAN HAL NIBS

PUZZLE 65

F H S F E DIE
TIRED HATRED I N
G R A E G LIES
CHAOS T DENY E M
T M T M Y
D WEAKER SCHEME
E H S R B L AXED
FRIGHT SLEUTH P A
E M U K O B A L R
N P POISON ATTACK
DUEL L D M C I E
RIDDLE PYTHON N
H B S E A
A E LIFE T TWIST
EVER I I E I H
O T MURDER SPEED
CRY P E Y E S

PUZZLE 69

LEARN TABLES B
E U A O PENCIL
S CLASSROOM N H A
S E S K H G A C
O R E SCHOOL L K
NIB M R M INK B
N SUBJECT E S O
F I L A E W H A
ART Y D A O SIR
N S C R D D
TEACHER H K R C
I A H D
INKWELL S S WRITE
I N P E L S
EDUCATION N D K
S E E R HISTORY
R T O E
HEADMASTER PEN

PUZZLE 62

B TYPE F
U V ISSUE A
FASHION X A C
I E K T EDIT R
H NEWS W F V S E
E E S NEWSPAPER P
A S L A U M R S O
LAST E T PRINT C R
T T H P L SPORT
HOME T E L Y O E
X E R E PAPER
FEATURE M E
I R S HEADLINES
R A P N I T
S L R A T T LOOK
TRAVEL G I R
T A EDITOR DIY
READERS N

PUZZLE 66

CREDIT A J
H R C CODES
E BALANCE U
Q A N O C R P
U N S U O N E
E K A NOMINAL T
C T P L VAT
SALE T S U P D Y
U I T U E C
R O E R B A
PAYMENTS RECEIPTS
L A H T H
U ENTRY TOTAL
S U U A S Y
A L X LEDGERS
VALUE A
S TAXRETURN

PUZZLE 70

SHOWER BAG TIMER D
H A A E R U R
A START T T A HASTE
V E T HURRY A H S
EXTRACARE E I S
O C A CORD I
SHOES H A D U IRON
U T M DRYER A G
I HOUSE J L L
TUB N U M SETS
RIGHT SOAP C
C U A T K LOOK
HOSE I R E M I S
A H R I FUSSING M
N P N P R H E
GROOMING D R T T
E N SHAMPOO SLIP
T R C
COORDINATE BUSINESS

PUZZLE 63

M JOLLY J
FESTIVE A GLOW
O U R S U A K
GRIN T T GIGGLE H
T N H H U
U Y ELATED COMIC
N A E O
AMUSE U R CHEERY
T M G H O
E I CHEERFUL FUN
L C S
HEAVEN G KISS L
X L L U
C M E EMBRACE
WIT PLEASED E K
T R GLAD Y
EUPHORIC A M
D Y JOY

PUZZLE 67

A S D
GROUND UNPACK E
A V R L I P
DRIVE E V O T O
D A PROPERTY COST
SELL T Y H I
N U HOUSE T
A E F N B
COTTAGES F E
I A T DETACHED
ROOMS A R R O R
N T M E M O
SALE FORSALE O
P I A V O M
GARAGE GATE BUY
I N E N F
PACK N MORTGAGE
E FLAT E E

PUZZLE 71

CHAMBERS SUBPOENA
O C D I Y
VETO I LEGAL C P
E C K U A A E
N COSTS I WAIVER
A L U WILL E M
N A BAR T P A I
TRIAL Y WRIT T
M E O V
D STATUTE PROOF
O U E E FEE U
COURT N S R C
K E U T OATH H
R T R C Y C
JURY LEGACY FACT
L A S S
SEALAW LENIENCE

PUZZLE 64

T JERSEY CAP
SUIT BRA A C L
T G L C RAINCOAT
O H O K I I A R
C TROUSERS WIG K U
K S S T H H N
I E BONNET K
N S TIE I G S
GOWN K MULE Y
S E B I E MAC
APRON N SHORTS
T O BIB T L K
E T E A MINI
DRESS KILT R P M
A T T D O
PANTS O F TRAIN
HIGHHEELS O
A Z

PUZZLE 68

N T D GUJARATI
O CATALAN T
R M N HINDI A
W I I C L
ENGLISH FLEMISH I
G E H L P A
I R J MANDARIN
ARMENIAN N N R
N A P M D I I
A N ARABIC S S
R N L C H H
BURMESE T G
S A S E L R
S G WELSH AZTEC
I Y E T E
A A I K
N ROUMANIAN

PUZZLE 72

BALANCE A T D
A R TANGENT O E
SOLID H G U R E S
I T I R MULTIPLY
S CHANCE E M
M A G R P M
SPEED LOGARITHM A E
C T V T C R T
INFINITE E A MASTER
E C N R L I Y
N D PROLATE T
CYCLOID A Y LINE
E U V R O I
RATIONAL TEST N N
C V S L R W S
ONE FINALITY ORBIT
N B E I O E
INFALLIBLE N O I
C E AGENT MAN

SOLUTIONS

PUZZLE 73

M
N FEATURE READ
MONEY D E D G
W LOVE C IDEAS
TIPS E I I E Z
R T COMPETITION
A ARTE E N
V E G READERS
EDITOR EDIT T
L N S F COOKERY
F L FIT L
O O A S ARTICLE
CARTOONS W S
A M K HOLIDAYS
S S I N U T
HEALTH O N WEEKLY
I N E I P
FAMILY PRINT E

PUZZLE 74

SILVER V L
C U I LILAC G
CAMEL BRONZE V R
R M Y L M BEIGE
BLUE YELLOW N Y
E ROSE T N D B
T A A C T CHERRY
L P H E R O
W D P O R F W
H P H C R MAROON
I INDIGO A W L
TAN R L CARNATION
E K E A O V
G C T T JADE
PRIMROSE T R M L
E E SAGE BAY I
VERDANT D E M
N M ORANGE

PUZZLE 75

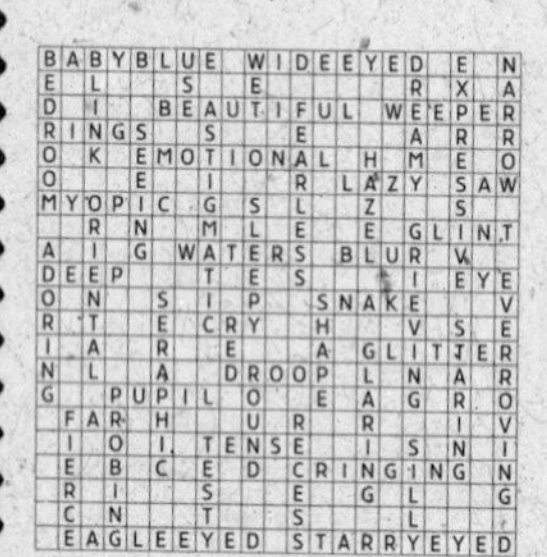

BABYBLUE WIDEEYED E N
E L S E R X A
D I BEAUTIFUL WEEPER
RINGS S E A R R
O K EMOTIONAL H M E O
O E I R LAZY SAW
MYOPIC G S L Z S
R N M L E E GLINT
A I G WATERS BLUR V
DEEP T E S I EYE
O N S I P SNAKE V
R T E CRY H V S E
I A R E A GLITTER
N L A DROOP L N A R
G PUPIL O E A G R O
FAR H U R R I V
I O I TENSE I S N I
E B C E D CRINGING N
R I S E G L G
C N T S L
EAGLEEYED STARRYEYED

PUZZLE 76

HOLIDAY VILLA
N S I U T
MEAL S X U
W AUSTRALIA U R
E N U E T BREAK
E D N SEA Y E
K O S Y
F R RELAX
PASSPORT I N
O U R V DRIVE
R N TRAVEL Y
T B N R P S C
U A DISCO O U O
G T G O COUNTRY
A H HEAT L H F
L E T S A U
TOURIST

PUZZLE 77

B GOOSE
SKUA U BUSTARD
Z B S P A
Z A E RHEA C W
BARNOWL R H
A R T C PARROT
V D A M R I O U P
O MOA E G W G E
COOT GREBE CHAT
E S B P P OWL R
T P L I E N I J E
GROUSE R N A L
E E DUNNOCK
R Y TERN I E K
O I V T D
COALTIT E HAWK
HERON W

PUZZLE 78

S KISSING K W
OWN N W UNISON
N O WED N N O
GUEST E TWINS
E C T W T HOLD
SINCERE COSY I O
R O O O SPORT
LOVE WARMTH I
I T D F S E N
M SMOOCH RING
PEACE R A O
E O CHAT PROTECT
TEAM L I A E I
BLOOD R SCOLD
M I S ARM N E
FIANCE O U TEA
X E KNOWING R

PUZZLE 79

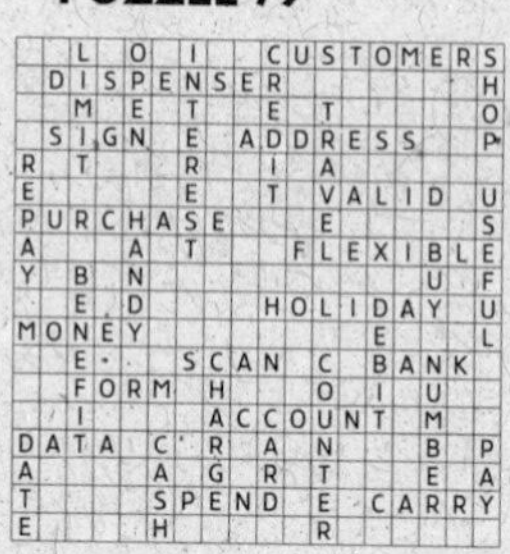

L O I CUSTOMERS
DISPENSER H
M E T E T O
SIGN E ADDRESS P
R T R I A
E E T VALID U
PURCHASE E S
A A T FLEXIBLE
Y B N U F
E D HOLIDAY U
MONEY E L
E SCAN C BANK
FORM H O I U
I ACCOUNT M
DATA C R A N B P
A A G R T E A
T SPEND E CARRY
E H R

PUZZLE 80

CLIFFS
O H
CHALK MARGATE
H S A A E
A CANTERBURY R P
S T I S D H
HYTHE V H E O
F A E CINQUE
O M PORT S
R F U LEEDS
DEAL CHANNEL
R W N DOCKS
ROMNEY KENT O A
A L O V S M
HILLS WYE T E
E D H N R LYDD
R WOODS E W
KNOLE P BAY
E SANDWICH Y

PUZZLE 81

B KEYBOARD
S BASS E R
MAJOR I Y P U
X W N P MINIM
O GUITAR T
P C A CLEF
RHYTHM N H L
O O O O U
N R CROTCHET
MELODY V G E
U S I A T
SONG O O NATURAL H
I O SCALES U O A
C T T I HORN M R
REFRAIN A E B T P
E L V R B OBOES
STAVE PLAY N N
T T S E E
INSTRUMENT

PUZZLE 82

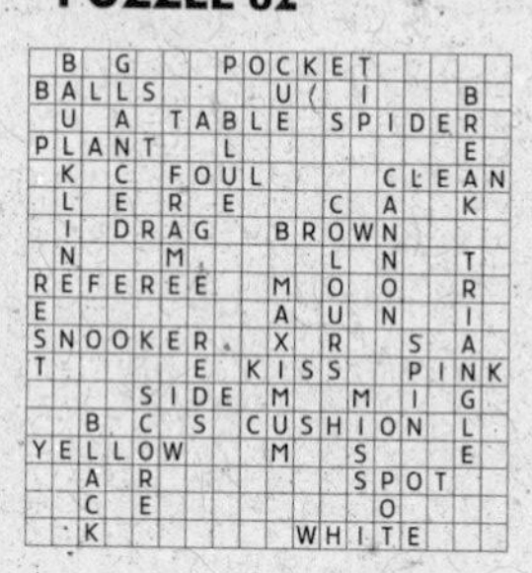

B G POCKET
BALLS U I B
U A TABLE SPIDER
PLANT L E
K C FOUL CLEAN
L E R E C A K
I DRAG BROWN
N M L N T
REFEREE M O O R
E A U N I
SNOOKER X R S A
T E KISS PINK
SIDE M M I G
B C S CUSHION L
YELLOW M S E
A R SPOT
C E O
K WHITE

PUZZLE 83

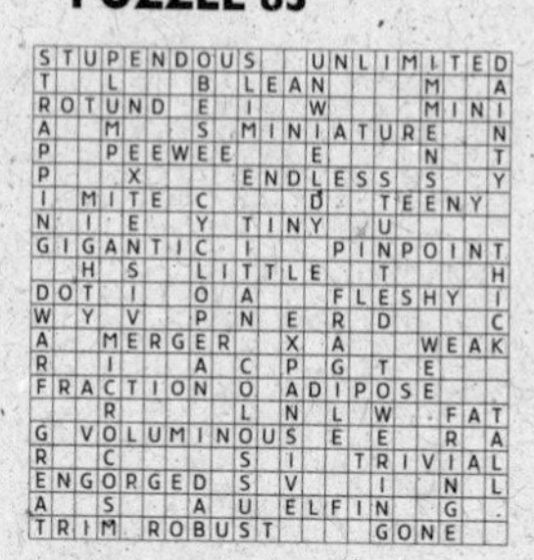

STUPENDOUS UNLIMITED
T L B LEAN M A
ROTUND E I W MINI
A M S MINIATURE N
P PEEWEE E N T
P X ENDLESS S Y
I MITE C D TEENY
N I E Y TINY U
GIGANTIC I PINPOINT
H S LITTLE T H
DOT I O A FLESHY I
W Y V P N E R D C
A MERGER X A WEAK
R I A C P G T E
FRACTION O ADIPOSE
R L N L W FAT
G VOLUMINOUS E E R A
R C S I TRIVIAL
ENGORGED S V I N L
A S A U ELFIN G
TRIM ROBUST GONE

PUZZLE 84

A A CORRECT HEAL
M T E A
ESTABLISH STEADY
N A T E
B DECIDE OVERHAUL
R H O R V E
A A CURE I M
CONNECT E C E
E C O P MEND D
H R R A O Y
COVER I OVERLAY
F R S R R F
A O A C R I
STILL D L A E X
T V J BIND FIX
E SECURE P A I
N E S PATCH
T T RIVET

SOLUTIONS

PUZZLE 85

PUZZLE 89

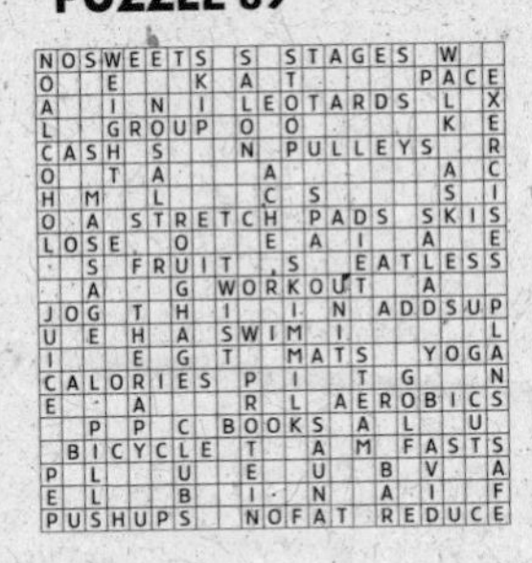

PUZZLE 93

```
E G S
DEPART CARRIAGES
O A A A G A T
O S W D N U O
R S S H H I A G K
STEAM I RIDE L E E
N O S S N R
F G K SEAT TENDER
U E E N L R
N R P G E F I F
NOSTALGIA I V U
E A N PRESERVE
LINE T E E R L
F R H
STATION ARRIVE C T
L R I U A O A
OIL SMELL N TRAIN
W L K
```

PUZZLE 86

PUZZLE 90

PUZZLE 94

```
D TEAPOT
C SINK S L
H S CUTLERY T
A S H R C HOB
DISH W C F T K W
R E A A DRAINER
SPLASHBACK I T L
F H I E C C P
H E N S C H L
COOKER DRAWER A
T T O N T
WINDOW C C E
A V F U KETTLES
T G E RANGE A O
E R N I I R B CUP
RAIL D T Y L K A
L GAS E N
SCALES E TAPS S
```

PUZZLE 87

PUZZLE 91

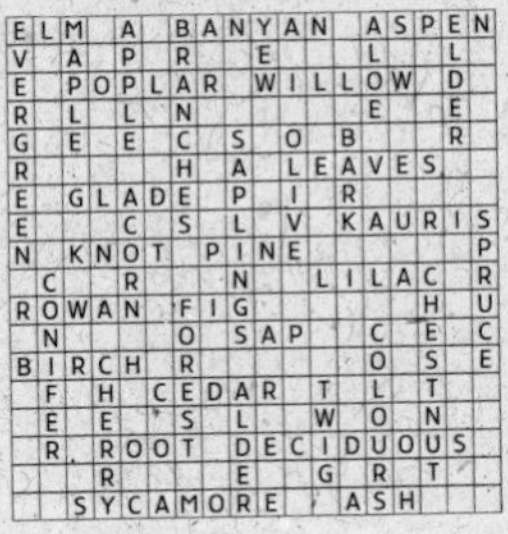

```
ELM A BANYAN ASPEN
V A P R E L L L
E POPLAR WILLOW D
R L L N E E
G E E C S O B R
R H A LEAVES
E GLADE P I R
E C S L V KAURIS
N KNOT PINE P
C R N LILAC R
ROWAN FIG H U
N O SAP C E C
BIRCH R O S E
F H CEDAR T L T
E E S L W O N
R ROOT DECIDUOUS
R E G R T
SYCAMORE ASH
```

PUZZLE 95

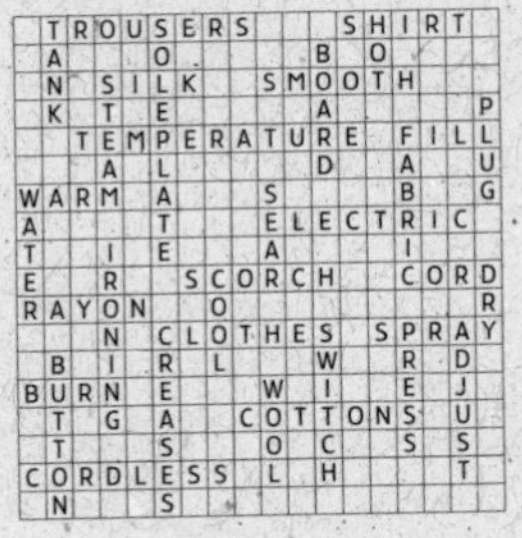

```
TROUSERS SHIRT
A O B O
N SILK SMOOTH
K T E A P
TEMPERATURE FILL
A L D A U
WARM A S B G
A T E ELECTRIC
T I E A I
E R SCORCH CORD
RAYON O R
N CLOTHES SPRAY
B I R L W R D
BURN E WI E J
T G A COTTONS U
T S O C S S
CORDLESS L H T
N S
```

PUZZLE 88

```
INSTRUMENTALIST
N O L A S
A O TELL L I
PAST C K EARN
P A RATE X C
R M R I O
OMEN CORN L M
P M E P
R LIRA X R
MILD O G T E
A R S N D H
T A TUNE HERE E
HELM T A N
L S I A IRIS
YELP I CUTE N I
N O C V
DREDGINGMACHINE
```

PUZZLE 92

```
COX O L HELM
A TOPSAIL E
N S E N AWASH P
VEER N REEF D O
A A P R L L R
S SLOOP O COAST
I O FOAM C U
CAPSIZE TACK B
K P R S S
S SAIL RIPTIDE
E H NAVY D A
CABIN U BELOW H
O P N B E A A
R S CREW B PROW
K HATCH R E D S
A STEWARD E
BUOY H M TAR
```

PUZZLE 96

```
C J H W
C E U BOATS H
PORRIDGE R T U E
R E A E G A
NIACIN BRAN MALT
F L L O K POUR
L Y W E
TASTY L A S M
K E S R L I
SERVING NUTRITION
S I E C E
START PACKET R
A G O A
F M Y SPOON MILK
I D C A S
B N IRON FRUIT
RAISINS R Z
E H NUTS EAT
```

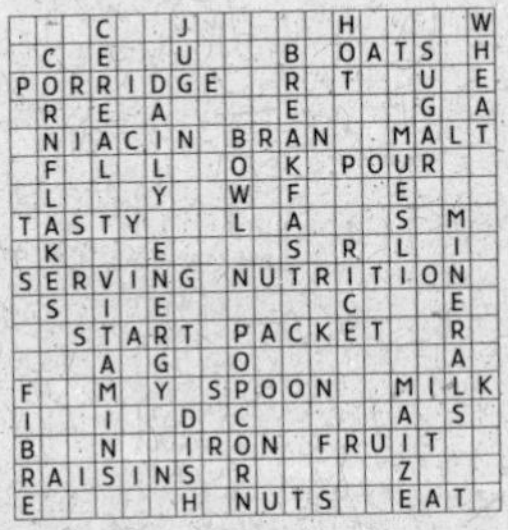

SOLUTIONS

PUZZLE 97

T COTTON R
E Y WOOL C
MACHINE T SOIL
P L Y STAIN L L I
E E L U T A O Q
R LOAD E T U U
A SPIN S WASHER I
T O N F A E E D
U CLEAN A T R D
R K N SHEET S
E S SHIRT R R D
POWDER
FABRIC L U R Y
O I WHITES Y I
A N S A N E N
M S O S E R PEGS
PREWASH VEST
K

PUZZLE 98

H P D F MISER
VISA ESTATE E
R Y A I R SUM
RETAIL RIG I
B A E ACT
PUBLIC CHORE L
N E L C W BID
P DEPOSIT E
TAX R U N L N
I TOKEN GROWTH
ADD F T T
U FEE SETTLE
DUE I A A E E
I CARTEL RENT
TRADE N E Y D

PUZZLE 99

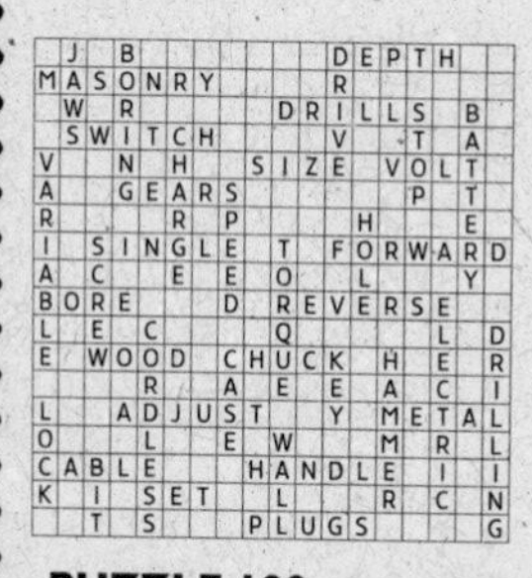

PUZZLE 100

PUZZLE 101

T C R V F T
CABLE REWIND O I
B E S C E I FRAME
FASTFORWARD W E
H R A R E A R
A R D PICTURE E
INSERT R T D R
D J STOP C A
SEEK G BUTTONS
E C S R A U E
T TAPE WATCH N
T M K T T
CASSETTE M VIDEO
D I E L M R P
J N MODE L
TUNE G A A
S DISPLAY
TRANSFER

PUZZLE 102

FRIENDS H
A HONGKONG
MOROCCO T S I
I O PLANE MEET
L A S I A A
Y C GREECE L
H P CITY
B JOURNEY H
E S R P E
A W MALTA R M
C I A A U E
THEMED Z S P
I I YACHT CAR
CRUISE O R
K R T PACK
E UNPACK E
T FLORIDA

PUZZLE 103

J BOLERO
TWOSTEP A N
S T W A L M E
CHACHA I VALETA S
I H S A D T
M A J T N H JIVE
MORRIS BEBOP S P
Y L G R O
E FANDANGO
BOSSANOVA P
O T RIGADOON
PIRQUETTE P
N A E M S
C FLING I A
A G R N M
PAULJONES RUMBA
E E E A
SARABAND LAVOLTA

PUZZLE 104

RECTANGLE A S
R DIAMOND P
ELLIPSE G G H
A HELIX LINE
POINT S E R
V G P O E
O L Y CONE ARC
LINEAR I T C
D ARROWS A E
M C POLYGON
C I L I O T
CURVED E R N R
U O A A E
BASE L OBLONG
E S B V
HEXAGON STAR
S X L

PUZZLE 105

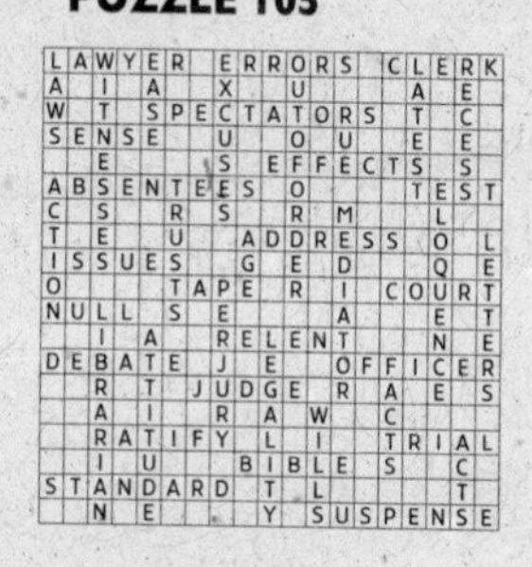

PUZZLE 106

T BALL D L
A LEO U C ARIES M
R R CHART B C A
FORTUNE K P E R O R
T E R TAURUS
SAGITTARIUS P
T E C S I
PALM O VIRGO
R I WORK G A
N E N N Q
I READ CASH U
F E L E A
O V T L CANCER
R P E H E L I
E I A PLANET U
CRYSTAL V HANDS
A C MONEY
S VENUS S
T S

PUZZLE 107

P L BENCH W
PARLIAMENT A E
R B COMMONS
T WOOLSACK T
AYES U M
P R C L H I
E H I O N
SPEAK A B U S
U K MEMBER SEAT
B E P B R M E E
LORDS E AGAINST R
I R L C
CHAIR D ELECT
E E L
WHIP P BIG FRONT
A L A O C O
LOBBY TOWER K R
L E E Y
NOES

PUZZLE 108

GEOGRAPHY GLACIER
R R L E S A
E A LIMESTONE L R
ALPS U O L AGE
T S V SEA OCEAN C
S PLAINS X G R D L
E A A I Y O A
A N MARSH S BAY
SAND O OASIS N
I POLES R O D
ARADA T I NORTH
L S E HAZES R E
T G TIN O T E R
ICE U COUNTRY R
T Y R O I BAR
U SCENERY R D I
D E A ICEBERGS
EARTH LOAM S E

SOLUTIONS

PUZZLE 109

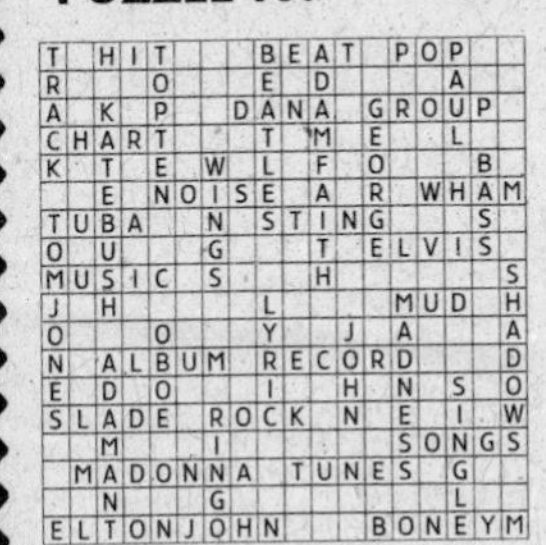

PUZZLE 110

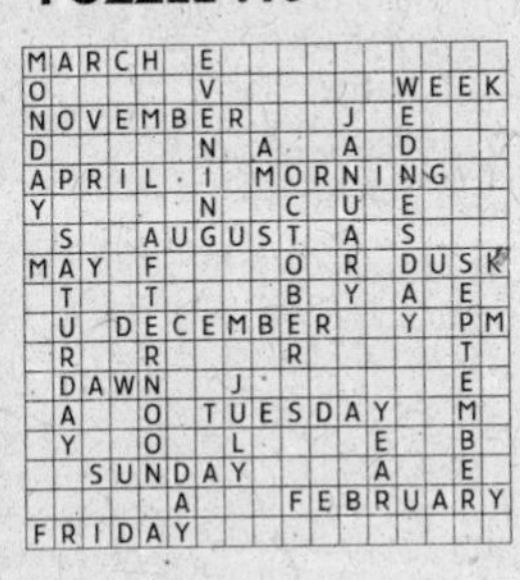

PUZZLE 111

PUZZLE 112

N	U	T	C	A	S	E		B		C			S			
U			I				H	O	B	O			T		G	
N			T			A		S		W		C	O	M	I	C
	T	W	I	T		C	A	S	U	A	L		I		G	
	Y		Z			E				R			C	O	O	K
	C		E		R		P	U	N	D	I	T			L	
B	O	U	N	C	E	R		P			N		F	O	O	L
	O				C			S			F		A			
K	N	O	W	A	L	L		T		W	I	T	N	E	S	S
			I		U			A			D				U	
L	O	U	T		S			R		H	E	R	E	T	I	C
	U			B	E	A	U	T	Y		L		G		T	
S	T	A	R			R				V			G		O	
	L		I		S	T	O	O	G	E		C	H	A	R	
N	A	V	V	Y		I		G		T			E			R
	W		A			S	E	R	F				A			A
			L			T		E		S	T	U	D	E	N	T

PUZZLE 113

T		U				B	R	I	D	L	E	P	A	T	H	S
R	A	N	K									L				T
A		D			R	I	D	E		B	O	A	T			A
I		E			O					U		N		S		T
N	A	R	R	O	W	B	O	A	T	S		E		H		I
		G												I		O
		R						S	A	I	L		S	P	I	N
	V	O	Y	A	G	E		U					P			
		U		I				B				C	A	N	A	L
A		N		R	A	I	L	W	A	Y			C			O
R		D		P				A					E			C
O			D	O	C	K		Y					T	R	E	K
A				R							C	A	R			
D	E	P	O	T			T		T		Y		A			T
		O					O		A		C		V			U
G	A	R	A	G	E		U		X		L		E			B
		T				C	R	U	I	S	E		L	I	N	E

PUZZLE 114

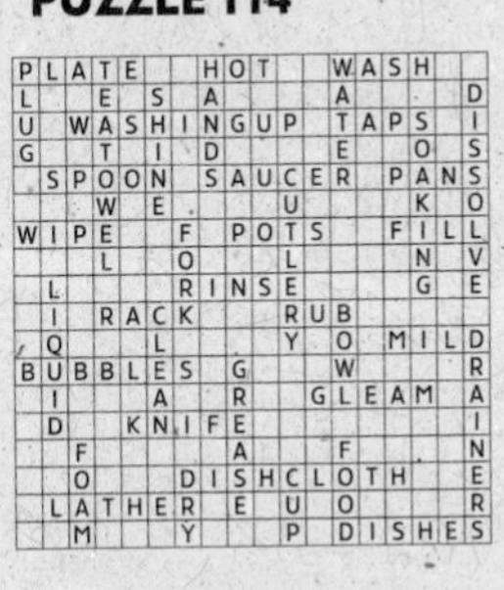

PUZZLE 115

PUZZLE 116

S	T	A	M	M	E	R		H	O	O	T		V	O	I	C	E			T
		R			X			E			I		E			H				A
		G	R	I	P	E		L	E	C	T	U	R	E		E	X	T	O	L
		U			R			L			T		B			E		W		K
L	I	E		R	E	S	P	O	N	S	E		A	V	E	R		A		I
					S		A				R		L					N		N
C	H	O	R	U	S		L	I	S	P		W	I	N	D	Y		G	A	G
O		D					A		P				Z		I				M	
N		E	C	H	O		V		E				E		S	P	O	K	E	
V			O		R		E		E						C				N	
E			M		D	I	R	E	C	T		S	H	O	U	T		A	S	K
R	E	C	I	T	E				H						S			V		
S			C		R	A	V	E							S		H	O	W	L
E		R			I			P	U	R	R	I	N	G				W		A
		E			N			I		A				A			P			N
C	A	L	L		G			T		N		J	A	B	B	E	R	I	N	G
L		A		R			M	A	N	T	R	A			L		A			U
U		T		E				P				W			U		T			A
C	H	I	R	P	S		S	H	U	S	H		B	E	R	A	T	I	N	G
K		N		L			A				U		O		T		L			E
S		G		Y	A	K	Y	A	K		M	O	O		S	W	E	A	R	

PUZZLE 117

PUZZLE 118

PUZZLE 119

R	A	M	P						S	A	M	P	L	E
E			A	T	H	L	E	T	E		A			A
S			S		E				M		G			G
T			T	R	A	D	I	T	I	O	N	S		L
I			E		T		R				E			E
N					E		O			S	T	A	R	S
G	A	T	H	E	R	I	N	G			I			
		A					M			O	C	C	U	R
		R					O					O		
C	A	T	E	R			N					M		
			A			A	G	R	E	E	A	B	L	E
F	A	I	R	Y			E		D					A
O			M				R		I		A			T
R		E	U	C	A	L	Y	P	T	U	S			A
E			F		R				O		I			B
S			F		I	G	N	O	R	E	D			L
T	E	A	S	E	D						E	A	S	E

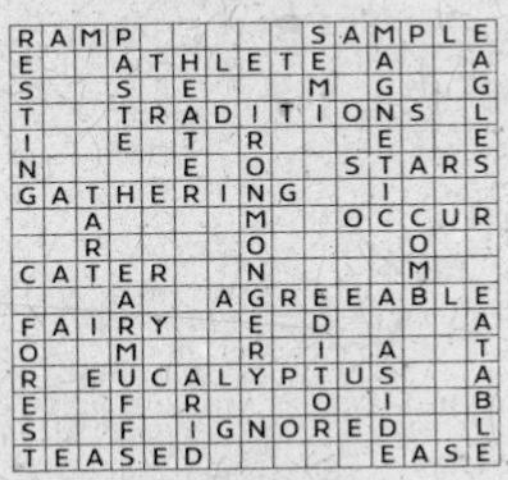

River: Humber.

PUZZLE 120

S	H	E	E	P	D	O	G							G			
	E						A					F	A	R	M	E	R
	D			C	O	T	T	A	G	E				E			
	G		S				E		R		S			E			
F	E	N	C	E		T			A		C	O	R	N			V
			A		T	R	E	E	S		E						I
S	P	I	R	E		A			S		N			H	I	L	L
			E			C	O	W			E				N		L
	B		C			T		I			R				N		A
	U		R		C	O	U	N	T	R	Y			S			G
	L		O			R		D				C	A	T	T	L	E
F	L	O	W	E	R			M				R		E			
I						S	T	I	L	E		O		E			C
E						H		L				P		P	A	T	H
L	A	N	E	S		E		L	A	M	B	S		L			U
D				H		E					A			E			R
		F	O	O	T	P	A	T	H		R						C
				P							N		B	E	N	C	H

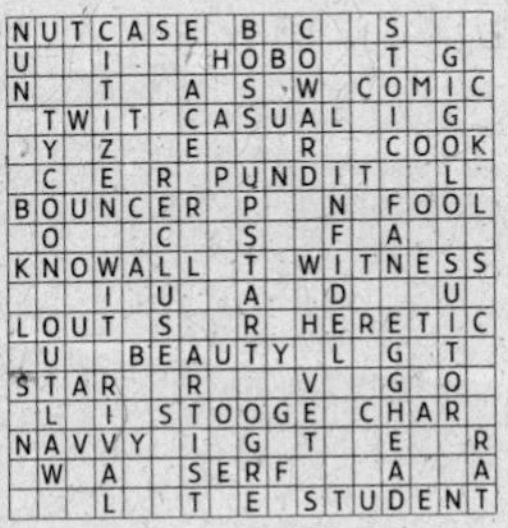

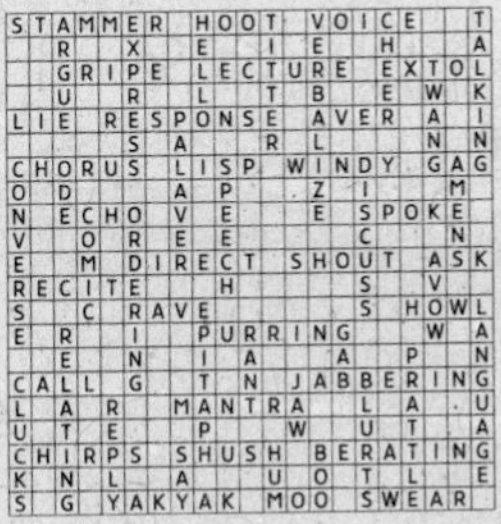

SOLUTIONS

PUZZLE 121

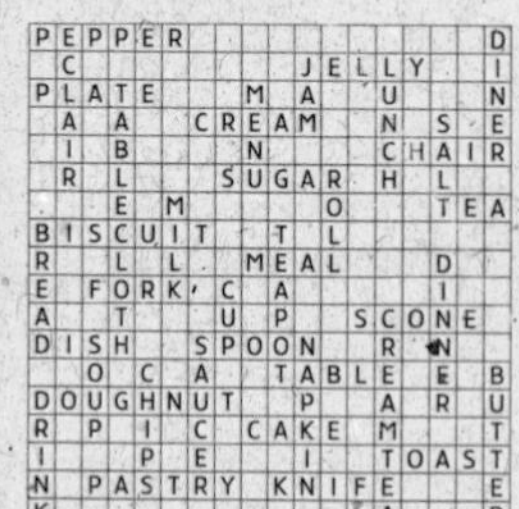

PEPPER D
C JELLY I
PLATE M A U N
A A CREAM N S E
I B N CHAIR
R L SUGAR H L
E M O TEA
BISCUIT T L
R L L MEAL D
E FORK C A I
A T U P SCONE
DISH SPOON R N
O C A TABLE E B
DOUGHNUT P A R U
R P I C CAKE M T
I P E I TOAST
N PASTRY KNIFE E
K A R

PUZZLE 122

H D H A THUNDER
LOWER O I O I
T Y AURORA WARM
T R R N E
E A WEATHER
RAINBOW D A
N SNOW I
CHILLY L WINDY
N WET C
MUGGY E BREEZE
U HEAT C
S L TYPHOON
TEMPEST L I
T M W D M
HAIL DEGREE I B
A N A S CLOUD
WASHOUT Y T Y S

PUZZLE 123

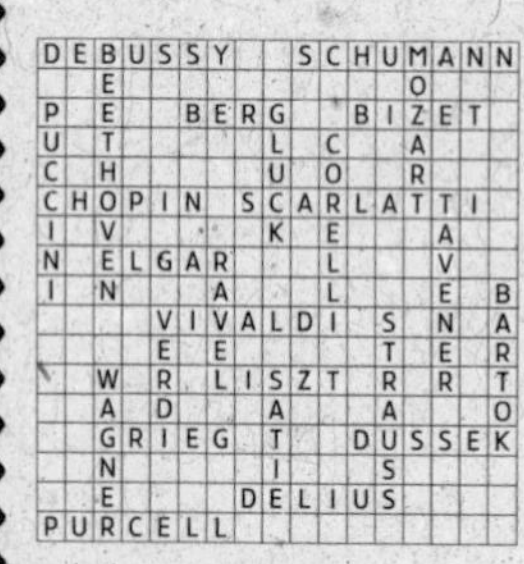

DEBUSSY SCHUMANN
E O
P E BERG BIZET
U T L C A
C H U O R
CHOPIN SCARLATTI
I V K E A
N ELGAR L V
I N A L E B
VIVALDI S N A
E E T E R
W R LISZT R R T
A D A A O
GRIEG T DUSSEK
N I S
E DELIUS
PURCELL

PUZZLE 124

SHEETS COUNT
I TOSS I
SNORE L G
S G D E T H
U PILLOWCASE QUILT
N R E R P R M
DRINK K YAWN LAY
R N C C R
E GOWN O FOURPOSTER
S S A V C I E
S K BEDROOM R S
SHEEP R A A P E T
I U L T Y D
SLEEP RELAX T J N
K T W DREAM I
R A E M G
O BLANKETS A H
DOUBLE E S SOFT
E D

PUZZLE 125

L G BREW M
HALLOWEEN T ICY
N O E FRIGHT S
T WEIRD E C T
E I A H I
TRICK E MIST F F
N A T E H SOUL Y
N H V LAMP L P
H D I E P E L U
CAULDRON E L M M
U E T I G L O P
N Y N H SPOOKY
T F GHOST N I
S I U C N
SPECTRE FLY FANGS
A S O S
SPIRIT BROOMSTICK
E M

PUZZLE 126

THEATRE COFFEE
O E C I N
WALK SHOPPING J
N T N E S O
F L A C R M CITY
R U U E A G
DINNER R L H B
E C A TRAVEL T O
N H N X A S U
D TAXI T T
SHOW BROWSE I
O R U Q
STATION E TRIP U
E BAR I E
GALLERY K VIEWS
A E
T CATHEDRAL

PUZZLE 127

MULLET DOVERSOLE T
I U O U V ANCHOR
SCAMPI L S E R E A
T P PILCHARDS CREW
S S H A H R L
MOUNTAINOUS W E I E
C N SEALION R
BASKINGSHARK L G S
A E O C BUSY
R R VESSELS L
Q E H A TURBOT
U SNAPPER R M E H
E E R FISHSTEW E
SEASONAL M A H N
B W P IONIANSEA
A N W I L L T U
RESORTS H N SOCKEYE T
E S KEDGE R E I
L L E ADMIRAL
I K PLUMB E U
CUTTLEFISH S S D S

PUZZLE 128

SCORE GREEN
N E C A E
O S H M X
O T PLAYERS T
K I M F
E N POCKET I
REDS K I A N
E O BLACK
CUSHION L L
U S BAIZE
E I R
O YELLOW
WINNER A R D
H R B K D POT
INTERVAL E W
T O L BROWN
E R L

PUZZLE 129

G B W F
HIGHCHAIR HAPPY E
R R S E
LULLABY TEETHED D
A H C I
U BABY W GRIN
G B O O C LAID A G
HEALTHY O L U W
T T TALK MILK
H L M I
B VEST NAPPY D
OIL O U R S
O POWDER A W
T W E S MITTENS
E RATTLE E O I M
E K R CRY G I
SLEEP PLAY H L
LAYETTE

PUZZLE 130

SLIPROAD R
H R JUNCTION
SLOW R O D
E N OVERTAKE FOG
R E W C U
V L B HILL T
DISTANCE E E S
C N A N TRAFFIC
VERGE ROAD V D
A J STEERED
ORBITALROAD L
E M L CLEAR
FAST SPEED I N
I E M E
SIGNS T VEHICLES P
N R A T X A
MAP JOIN DRIVER
L L T K

PUZZLE 131

H SHOW
SKIT D I PACE
T T U SCENE L
FAN HERO G A
G FLAT L MASK
SET V PODIUM S
T FLOOR E D I
U O C E A SKETCH
N Y ASIDE C O
TALENT E P S O U
M R N ACTOR S
A FASTEN A CUE
STAR P FLOP S
E R IDOL SHY
U COMIC I R E
PROP L L JEER
EXIT P

PUZZLE 132

NONSENSE QUIPS C
U M N U PUNCH
T I MISCHIEF O I
SILLY C R O O C
N E KNACK LIFTS A
A C E A L L A N
N HORSEPLAY GLEE
TEASE C C S R
R N ESCAPADE COMEDY
I T R M O R I
C I SPORTIVE ROMP
KICK L T ACT L
I A PAYS M H E
GOOD U R S P A
A G A C GAGS
M WISH N JOLLY R E
B O TICKLE A A O
O R E S PARADES
LUDICROUS T S N Y

SOLUTIONS

PUZZLE 133

```
LEARN TABLES     B
E  U A  O   PENCIL
S CLASSROOM  N H A
S  E S  K  H G A C
O  R E  SCHOOL L K
NIB  M R   M INK B
 N SUBJECT E S   O
 F I L A E W H   A
 ART Y D A O   SIR
 N  S    C R D   D
 TEACHER H K R C  
    I        A H D
INKWELL S  S WRITE
  I N   P  E   L S
 EDUCATION N   D K
  S E E R HISTORY 
      R T  O   E  
  HEADMASTER PEN  
```

PUZZLE 134

```
COCKINGTON SHOPS   
A L   A    I  A    
RAIL  RESORT HILLS 
S F   D       G    
  F THEATRE T N T  
 S    N     O T O  
 ENGLISH  HARBOUR P
 A  I       Q N B A
    G   H   U  SAND
BRIXHAM O  WALK Y D
E   T   T   Y  W  L
ROADS   E     BATHE
R B    CLIMATE T   
Y BOAT O  A    E   
H E  RIVIERA PARK  
E Y  E E  I  I     
A  VIEW   N BEACH  
D    S   BAY R     
```

PUZZLE 135

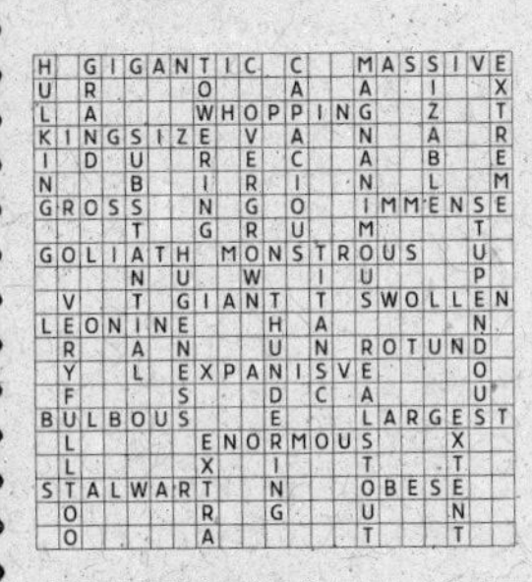

```
H GIGANTIC C  MASSIVE
U R    O   A  A  I  X
L A    WHOPPING  Z  T
KINGSIZE V A  N  A  R
I D U  R E C  A  B  E
N   B  I R I  N  L  M
GROSS  N G O  IMMENSE
    T  G R U  M    T 
GOLIATH MONSTROUS  U 
    N U  W  I U    P 
 V  T GIANT T SWOLLEN
LEONINE   H A      N 
 R  A N   U N ROTUND 
 Y  L EXPANISVE    O 
 F    S   D C A    U 
BULBOUS   E   LARGEST
 L     ENORMOUS   X  
 L     X  I   T   T  
STALWART  N   OBESE  
 O     R  G   U   N  
 O     A      T   T  
```

PUZZLE 136

```
  S      D         
GATES  FIRSTCLASS  
  E  R   I  O      
GRADIENT V  ARRIVED
U M  L   E  L A I E
A  PLATFORM   I A P
R  O X     MAIL D A
D  I   D   E    U R
 C N  TIMETABLE C T
PORTER E   L    T  
 A S   S           
 C   SLEEPERS B D  
 HALT  L  N   R R  
   I S    G BRITISH
SIGNAL TRAIN   D N 
E  E O R  N   G K  
A    W I  EXPRESS  
TRACK  P           
       STATIONS    
```

PUZZLE 137

```
       GAMBIT D C
D  W   A A  H I A
R CHECKMATE I A S
A  I H E E KNIGHT
WAIT E  C   K O L
   E SQUARES  N E
 B   S  P   PLAY 
CLOCK N TIME  L B
 A    O U O     O
 COMPUTER V     A
 K    A E E Q B R
  R P T   STUDIED
 POSITION   E S  
  O E O   T E H K
  K C N  PAWN O I
    E     K   PIN
RULES PROJECT   G
```

PUZZLE 138

```
 R B  S  MATCH  S 
DAYLIGHT    O   E 
 D A  I F SPARKLED
 I Z  M L   L  A A
TAPER M A  G SUNNY
 N   BEAM  L   T  
STAR  R E CANDLE E
U  A     L R   R L
N  Y BONFIRE   N E
LIT F    G   G   C
I   L B  HEADLIGHT
G FLARE  T   I L R
H I S A      S O I
TORCH C BRIGHT W C
  E   O    L E    
 G  SUNSHINE NEON 
 A  U      A      
 SHINE ILLUMINATE 
```

PUZZLE 139

```
 J  CAROL G   B  W
SARAH   I W JOAN E
 N  R JULIET  R  N
DEBBIE  Y N   B  D
 T  S    U   SALLY
    T    N    R A 
SYLVIA  VANESSA U 
  U N      M    R 
D CLEO     M  P A 
IVY     M PAM A   
A  SANDRA E   U J 
N  H  A U N EILEEN
ALMA MILDRED  I N 
   R  S E L ANN N 
DOROTHY   O L E I 
O  N    J P I   F 
R     FLORENCE  E 
ANGELA  Y   E MARY
```

PUZZLE 140

```
 R   F      JACK R
BOOKMAKERS T   A O
 Y E C   A Y CURLY
 SUNITA  L R   E  
 R   O  ALLOTMENTS
JOE FRED Y N     A
 L   Y E  VERA   R
 L K  KIRK  O  B A
 STEVE R  DEV BETH
   V   D P  E  T  
JANICE R E  R R   
 U N  BETTY SHOP  
 D       E  R S   
 RITA  GARAGE I  C
 E A   A    T EMMA
 Y X EMILY  U  I F
   I   L    R  K E
 JASON  KABIN LES 
```

PUZZLE 141

```
SHOES   M F R W  
 E  TAFFETA APRON
 M  A   S B G A A
  O Y  SHORTS P P
G U       I      
ATTIRE  G COSTUME
R F   S A   T    
TWINSET RIBBON  C
E T H U M O L G O
R  GIRDLE OVERALL
    R   N T   L L
SWEATER T  ANGORA
      A       S R
H M TIGHTS  B H  
A I I L O   E  T 
TUNIC APPAREL  I 
  I K N S   TWEED
```

PUZZLE 142

```
CAW    BLEATS      
L HOWL L    W MOANS
A I  I A  CHIME   N
T RAPS R  H S WHINE
T R  PEEP E H   O E
E       U E     O Z
RUMBLE  R P  RATTLE
   A CHIRPS  O     
   W H   E  BABBLES
 BELLOW  A   R L   
 A    H CLICKS A   
 YELP I O      SIGH
    I SNORT F  T   
PLUMP P   ALARMS   
R   E E B P N U    
A   SCREAMS F RINGS
TICK A  R   A M    
E R  L  K   R U    
  YELL  SNORE R    
```

PUZZLE 143

```
MATCHMAKER PASSION
 T H E     R C  N 
 TWO EMBRACE ROSES
 R O T L N T E    
LADS  KISS T E    
 C E   N W Y N Q  
 T  CUDDLE     U C
    O  D ROMANCE O
HUMOUR A       S U
A A R  T    CHATUP
N N THREE   H  I L
D    U      A LOVE
S GORGEOUS  R  N  
O I       WOMAN   
M R   P   I D    M
E LASSES  N BOYS A
  S   C     R    L
   PICK     FEMALE
```

PUZZLE 144

```
SUMMER  SOON DATE  
U A O   P  O E  R Y
N NONCE R TWICE AGE
DAY   V I H  A  S S
A MILLENNIUM D    T
Y O  E  G R  E YORE
 MOMENTS  S M   F R
  N  T  D D I S T D
DUSK   MAYANDJUNE A
A   P   Y Y N N N Y
WINTER  B   I U    
N O R MORNING PAST 
  O I I E   H  N   
SUNDOWN A AFTERNOON
E   D U K      U N 
C  W  T  T  Y  A C 
O SEPTEMBER EARLIER
N  E     R  A      
DARK DECEMBER      
```

SOLUTIONS

PUZZLE 145

	S							M				J	I	V	E		
C	H	A	R	L	E	S	T	O	N			I				F	
	I		O					R		B	E	G	U	I	N	E	
	M	I	N	U	E	T		R		O						E	
	M		D					I		L		V	A	L	E	T	A
	Y		O		C	H	A	S	S	E							
						O				R		C		B			
T	U	R	N			R			P	O	L	O	N	A	I	S	E
W		E				N						N		L			
O	N	E	S	T	E	P		T				G	A	L	L	O	P
S		L				I		A				A					I
T					S	P	I	N			T				F		R
E				C		E		G			W	H	I	R	L		O
P	O	L	K	A				O			I				I		U
				N							R		D	A	N	C	E
	C	H	A	C	H	A					L				G		T
		O		A				T	W	I	S	T					T
B	O	P		N										M	O	V	E

PUZZLE 146

	B		G				P	O	C	K	E	T					
B	A	L	L	S					U			I				B	
	U		A		T	A	B	L	E		S	P	I	D	E	R	
P	L	A	N	T			L									E	
	K		C		F	O	U	L					C	L	E	A	N
	L		E		R		E				C		A			K	
	I		D	R	A	G			B	R	O	W	N				
	N				M						L		N			T	
R	E	F	E	R	E	E			M		O		O			R	
E									A		U		N			I	
S	N	O	O	K	E	R			X		R			S		A	
T						E		K	I	S	S			P	I	N	K
				S	I	D	E		M			M		I		G	
		B		C		S		C	U	S	H	I	O	N		L	
Y	E	L	L	O	W				M			S				E	
		A		R								S	P	O	T		
		C		E									O				
		K								W	H	I	T	E			

PUZZLE 147

			F				L	I	M	E		D				
	G	O	L	D		S			A		M	A	U	V	E	
			E			I			P			M				S
	P	A	S	T	E	L			L	I	L	A	C			E
T			H			V			E			S		L		P
H		B		C	R	E	A	M		F		K	H	A	K	I
E		U				R		A		A				V		A
M	A	R	O	O	N			G		W	H	I	T	E		
E		G				G	R	E	E	N				N		B
		U	M	B	E	R		N				F	U	D	G	E
B		N				E		T		P				E		I
R	U	D	D	Y		Y		A	Z	U	R	E		R		G
O		Y		E			H			R			S			E
W			F	L	A	M	E			P	E	W	T	E	R	
N				L			N			L			E			
	B	L	O	O	M		N			E		T	E	A	K	
				W		P	A	L	E				L			